INTERNATIONAL ATOMIC WEIGHTS

NAME	SYM-BOL	ATOMIC NUMBER	ATOMIC WEIGHT*	NAME	SYM-BOL	ATOMIC NUMBER	ATOMIC WEIGHT*
Actinium	Ac	89	227	Mercury			
Aluminum	Al	13	26.98	Molybdenum			
Americium	Am	95	[243]	Neodymium			
Antimony	Sb	51	121.76	Neon			
Argon	Ar	18	39.944	Neptunium			
Arsenic	As	33	74.91	Nickel	Ni		58.71
Astatine	At	85	[210]	Niobium	Nb	41	92.91
Barium	Ba	56	137.36	Nitrogen	N	7	14.008
Berkelium	Bk	97	[249]	Nobelium	No	102	[253]
Beryllium	Be	4	9.013	Osmium	Os	76	190.2
Bismuth	Bi	83	209.00	Oxygen	O	8	16.0000
Boron	B	5	10.82	Palladium	Pd	46	106.4
Bromine	Br	35	79.916	Phosphorus	P	15	30.975
Cadmium	Cd	48	112.41	Platinum	Pt	78	195.09
Calcium	Ca	20	40.08	Plutonium	Pu	94	[242]
Californium	Cf	98	[249]	Polonium	Po	84	210
Carbon	C	6	12.011	Potassium	K	19	39.100
Cerium	Ce	58	140.13	Praseodymium	Pr	59	140.92
Cesium	Cs	55	132.91	Promethium	Pm	61	[145]
Chlorine	Cl	17	35.457	Protactinium	Pa	91	231
Chromium	Cr	24	52.01	Radium	Ra	88	226.05
Cobalt	Co	27	58.94	Radon	Rn	86	222
Columbium: see Niobium †				Rhenium	Re	75	186.22
Copper	Cu	29	63.54	Rhodium	Rh	45	102.91
Curium	Cm	96	[245]	Rubidium	Rb	37	85.48
Dysprosium	Dy	66	162.51	Ruthenium	Ru	44	101.1
Einsteinium	Es	99	[254]	Samarium	Sm	62	150.35
Erbium	Er	68	167.27	Scandium	Sc	21	44.96
Europium	Eu	63	152.0	Selenium	Se	34	78.96
Fermium	Fm	100	[255]	Silicon	Si	14	28.09
Fluorine	F	9	19.00	Silver	Ag	47	107.880
Francium	Fr	87	[223]	Sodium	Na	11	22.991
Gadolinium	Gd	64	157.26	Strontium	Sr	38	87.63
Gallium	Ga	31	69.72	Sulfur	S	16	32.066§
Germanium	Ge	32	72.60	Tantalum	Ta	73	180.95
Gold	Au	79	197.0	Technetium	Tc	43	[99]
Hafnium	Hf	72	178.50	Tellurium	Te	52	127.61
Helium	He	2	4.003	Terbium	Tb	65	158.93
Holmium	Ho	67	164.94	Thallium	Tl	81	204.39
Hydrogen	H	1	1.0080	Thorium	Th	90	232.05
Indium	In	49	114.82	Thulium	Tm	69	168.94
Iodine	I	53	126.91	Tin	Sn	50	118.70
Iridium	Ir	77	192.2	Titanium	Ti	22	47.90
Iron	Fe	26	55.85	Tungsten	W	74	183.86
Krypton	Kr	36	83.80	Uranium	U	92	238.07
Lanthanum	La	57	138.92	Vanadium	V	23	50.95
Lead	Pb	82	207.21	Xenon	Xe	54	131.30
Lithium	Li	3	6.940	Ytterbium	Yb	70	173.04
Lutetium	Lu	71	174.99	Yttrium	Y	39	88.92
Magnesium	Mg	12	24.32	Zinc	Zn	30	65.38
Manganese	Mn	25	54.94	Zirconium	Zr	40	91.22
Mendelevium	Md	101	[256]				

* A value given in brackets is the mass number of the most stable known isotope.

† The English name of this element has been changed recently, by action of the International Union of Pure and Applied Chemistry.

§ Because of natural variations in the relative abundance of the isotopes of sulfur the atomic weight of this element has a range of ±0.003.

COLLEGE CHEMISTRY

A Series of Chemistry Texts

LINUS PAULING, EDITOR

General Chemistry, *Second Edition*
LINUS PAULING

College Chemistry, *Second Edition*
LINUS PAULING

College Chemistry in the Laboratory, No. 1
LLOYD E. MALM AND HARPER W. FRANTZ

College Chemistry in the Laboratory, No. 2
LLOYD E. MALM AND HARPER W. FRANTZ

A Laboratory Study of Chemical Principles, *Second Edition*
HARPER W. FRANTZ

Introductory Quantitative Analysis
AXEL R. OLSON, EDWIN F. ORLEMANN, AND CHARLES W. KOCH

Introductory Quantitative Chemistry
AXEL R. OLSON, CHARLES W. KOCH, AND GEORGE C. PIMENTEL

COLLEGE
CHEMISTRY

*An Introductory Textbook
of General Chemistry*

SECOND EDITION

by LINUS PAULING

Professor of Chemistry in the California Institute of Technology

Illustrations by ROGER HAYWARD

 W. H. FREEMAN AND COMPANY

San Francisco and London

TO

DR. THOMAS ADDIS

who in applying science
to medicine
kept always uppermost
his deep sympathy
for mankind

Preface to the Second Edition

In the preparation of the second edition of this book an effort has been made to increase the clarity of the presentation of the subject. The first part of the book has been largely revised in such a way that the facts, concepts, and theories of chemistry are introduced more gradually and more systematically than in the first edition. Some new, rather simple illustrative exercises are given in the text, immediately following the sections that they illustrate. The exercises at the ends of the chapters have also been considerably revised, with elimination of some of the more difficult ones. Answers are given to many of the exercises that involve calculations.

The sequence of chapters has been changed to increase the systematization of the subject. The book has been divided into six parts, and, in order that the student may be helped to keep himself oriented during the year, each part is provided with an introduction, describing the chapters contained within this part and telling why the subjects in these chapters are being taken up at that place in the course.

Part I, which constitutes an introduction to the subject, deals with both descriptive chemistry and elementary chemical theory. Theoretical chemistry is taken up more thoroughly in Part II, Chapters 8 to 12, and Part IV, Chapters 17 to 23. In Part III, Chapters 13 to 16, there is given a discussion of the chemistry of a number of the non-metallic elements, as systematized by theoretical principles; and the nature of metals and alloys, metallurgy, and the chemistry of many metals are discussed in Part V, Chapters 24 to 29. Part VI consists of two chapters on chemical substances related to living organisms and one chapter on nuclear chemistry.

There has been a significant increase in the amount of organic chemistry in the book. In Chapter 7, on carbon and the compounds of carbon, there is a detailed discussion of the paraffin hydrocarbons, hydrocarbons containing double and triple bonds, organic isomers, the chloromethanes, alcohols, ethers, and organic acids, and a brief discussion of the chemical reactions of organic substances. Organic substances are also discussed, together with inorganic substances, in several other chapters of the book, in connection with the theories of chemistry. Chapter 30, Organic Chemistry, and Chapter 31, Biochemistry, deal exclusively with organic substances.

Chapter 3, The Electron and the Nuclei of Atoms, is a new chapter, designed to help the student to understand the electronic theory of molecular structure, upon which modern chemistry is based. In this chapter a non-mathematical account is given of some of the experiments carried out during the period of twenty years commencing about 1895 which led to the discovery of the electron and of the nuclei of atoms and the measurement of the properties of these fundamental particles. The electronic structure of atoms is then discussed in Chapter 5, in connection with the periodic table. Oxidation-reduction reactions and valence are introduced in a simple way in Chapter 6, preliminary to the more detailed discussion of these subjects and of the electronic theory of molecular structure given in Chapters 10, 11, and 12.

Many of my colleagues in the California Institute of Technology and many other teachers of chemistry have given advice during the preparation of this edition, and it is a pleasure for me to express my gratitude to them. I thank especially Professor F. J. Allen, of Purdue University, and Professor Ogden Baine, of Southern Methodist University, for their help.

LINUS PAULING

Pasadena, California
23 March 1955

Preface to the First Edition

The fundamental principles underlying the planning of the present book have been expressed in the preface of my earlier textbook, "General Chemistry, An Introduction to Descriptive Chemistry and Modern Chemical Theory," published three years ago. The first two paragraphs of the Preface of "General Chemistry" summarize these principles:

"Chemistry is a very large subject, which continues to grow, as new elements are discovered or made, new compounds are synthesized, and new principles are formulated. Nevertheless, despite its growth, the science can now be presented to the student more easily and effectively than ever before. In the past the course in general chemistry has necessarily tended to be a patch-work of descriptive chemistry and certain theoretical topics. The progress made in recent decades in the development of unifying theoretical concepts has been so great, however, that the presentation of general chemistry to the students of the present generation can be made in a more simple, straightforward, and logical way than formerly.

"For example, every boy now knows about atoms, and accepts them as part of his world—they are split in the atomic bomb and in the comic papers, they stare at him from advertisements. In this book I begin the teaching of chemistry by discussing the properties of substances in terms of atoms and molecules. The subject is then developed in as orderly a manner as has seemed possible at the present stage of chemical knowledge."

Although "General Chemistry" was written primarily for use by students planning to major in chemistry and related fields, it has been found useful also by students with primary interest in other subjects, including some who have not received instruction in chemistry in high school. Experience has shown, however, that there is need for a book based on the approach of "General Chemistry," but written in a more slowly paced, less mathematical form. The present book, "College

Chemistry," provides this more gradual introduction to modern chemistry. I propose, in the near future, to revise "General Chemistry" in such a way as to make it especially suited to use by first-year college students who plan to major in chemistry and by other well-prepared students with a special interest in the subject.

The present book does not present any change in point of view from the earlier one. Some of the chapters, especially those dealing with elementary theory, have been incorporated with little change. The effort has been made to introduce all new concepts gradually, with satisfactorily thorough discussion and precise definition. The treatment of the more advanced theoretical subjects has been simplified. Use is made of no mathematics but elementary algebra, and instruction is given in the ratio method of solving problems. The treatment of the gas laws has been completely revised, and the chapter devoted to gases has been moved forward. Descriptive chemistry has been introduced more gradually, with more thorough discussion of the chemistry of the common elements, especially hydrogen, oxygen, nitrogen, and carbon. A chapter on biochemistry, a discussion of color photography, and some other new features have been introduced.

In general, new technical words and terms are defined in the text. Use has also been made of some other words with which the student may not be familiar; it may occasionally be necessary for him to find the meaning of one of these words by looking it up in the dictionary. It is my hope that every student who reads the book will benefit by an increase in his general vocabulary as well as in his scientific vocabulary, and also by an increase in the precision and soundness of his thinking about non-scientific questions as well as about scientific questions.

I am indebted for assistance in various ways in the preparation of the book to Dr. Philip A. Shaffer, Jr., Prof. Norman Davidson, Prof. Ernest H. Swift, Prof. F. O. Koenig, Prof. Harper W. Frantz, Prof. Lloyd E. Malm, Mr. Linus Pauling, Jr., Mr. Peter J. Pauling, Dr. Eugene K. Maun, Miss Selina Weinbaum, and especially Mr. Roger Hayward, the illustrator. I also thank Dr. R. W. G. Wyckoff, Dr. D. S. Clark, Dr. S. Kyropoulos, Prof. C. E. Hall, Dr. J. A. Leermakers, the Malleable Founders' Society, and the Griffith Observatory for providing figures. I am further indebted to Prof. L. H. Farinholt, Prof. J. A. Timm, Prof. F. E. Blacet, Prof. J. F. Baxter, and many other teachers of chemistry who have made suggestions of ways in which my earlier book could be improved.

LINUS PAULING

February 28, 1950

Table of Contents

PART ONE

An Introduction to Modern Chemistry

Chemistry is a complex subject, and it is hard for a teacher to find a logical order in which to present it. Chemistry is the investigation and discussion of the properties of substances—of thousands of different substances. A part of chemistry, called *descriptive chemistry*, consists in the tabulation of the properties of substances as observed or as found by experiment. Another part, *theoretical chemistry*, consists in the formulation of principles that systematize and correlate the facts of descriptive chemistry.

Both theoretical chemistry and descriptive chemistry are presented in this book, in a sequence that has been designed to help you to understand the principles and to remember the facts of chemistry.

The book is divided into six parts. Part I, Chapters 1 to 7, constitutes an introduction to modern chemistry. In Chapter 1 some fundamental concepts and definitions relating to kinds of substances are presented. In Chapter 2, on the atomic structure of matter, there is a discussion of the way in which substances are built out of atoms, and the relation between the properties of substances and their atomic structure. The atoms themselves are known to be built of electrons and atomic nuclei; the nature of the electron and of the nuclei of atoms is presented in Chapter 3. The classification of substances into elements and compounds is discussed in Chapter 4. In Chapter 5, on the chemical elements and the periodic law, an important system of classification of the elements is described; and in the following two chapters this system is used as the basis for the discussion of the chemistry of some of the elements.

1

The background of knowledge of chemical facts provided by these chapters will then enable you to embark upon the study of some further aspects of theoretical chemistry, in Part II, Chapters 8 to 12. Part III, Chapters 13 to 16, presents a discussion of the chemistry of a number of additional elements, as systematized by theoretical principles. Part IV consists of seven chapters dealing mainly with theoretical subjects. The nature of metals and alloys and the chemistry of many metals are discussed in Part V, Chapters 24 to 29. Two chapters on the chemical substances related to living organisms and one chapter on nuclear chemistry constitute the concluding section, Part VI.

Chemistry is not something that exists only between the covers of a textbook. It is an important part of man's effort to understand the world in which we live, and to obtain a mastery of natural forces. I hope that, as you continue your study of chemistry, you will find pleasure in having a better understanding of the nature of the world and of the phenomena that take place about you, and that when you come to the end of this book and of your course in chemistry you will feel that the efforts that you have made to master the subject have been justified by the enlargement of your mental horizons.

Chapter 1

Chemistry and
Matter

The rapid progress true Science now makes occasions my regretting sometimes that I was born so soon. It is impossible to imagine the heights to which may be carried, in a thousand years, the power of man over matter. O that moral Science were in as fair a way of improvement, that men would cease to be wolves to one another, and that human beings would at length learn what they now improperly call humanity.—

BENJAMIN FRANKLIN,
in a letter to the chemist Joseph Priestley, 8 February 1780.

Why study chemistry? An important reason is indicated in the foregoing statement by Benjamin Franklin—it is through chemistry and her sister sciences that the power of man, of mind, over matter is obtained. Nearly two hundred years ago Franklin said that science was making rapid progress. We know that the rate of progress of science has become continually greater, until now the nature of the world in which we live has been greatly changed, through scientific and technical progress, from that of Franklin's time.

Science plays such an important part in the modern world that no one can now feel that he understands the world in which he lives unless he has an understanding of science.

The science of chemistry deals with *substances*. At this point in the study of chemistry we shall not define the word substance in its scientific sense, but shall assume that you have a general idea of what the word means. Common examples of substances are water, sugar, salt, copper, iron, oxygen—you can think of many others.

A century and a half ago it was discovered by an English chemist, Sir Humphry Davy (1778–1829), that common salt can be separated, by passing electricity through it, into a soft, silvery metal, to which he gave

3

the name sodium, and a greenish-yellow gas, which had been discovered some time earlier, and named chlorine. Chlorine is a corrosive gas, which attacks many metals, and irritates the mucous membranes of the nose and throat if it is inhaled. The discovery that salt is composed of a metal (sodium) and a corrosive gas (chlorine), and that the properties of salt are quite different from those of sodium or chlorine is one of the many surprising facts about the nature of substances that chemists have discovered.

A sodium wire will burn in chlorine, producing salt. The process of combination of sodium and chlorine to form salt is called a *chemical reaction*. Ordinary fire also involves a chemical reaction, the combination of the fuel with oxygen in the air to form the products of combustion. For example, gasoline contains compounds of carbon and hydrogen, and when a mixture of gasoline and air explodes (burns rapidly) in the cylinders of an automobile a chemical reaction takes place, in which the gasoline and the oxygen of the air react to form carbon dioxide and water vapor (plus a small amount of carbon monoxide), and at the same time to release the energy that moves the automobile. Carbon dioxide and carbon monoxide are compounds of carbon and oxygen, and water is a compound of hydrogen and oxygen.

Chemists study substances, in order to learn as much as they can about their properties (their characteristic qualities) and about the reactions that change them into other substances. Knowledge obtained in this way has been found to be extremely valuable. It not only satisfies man's curiosity about himself and about the world in which he lives, but it also can be applied to make the world a better place to live in, to make people happier, by raising their standards of living, ameliorating the suffering due to ill health, and enlarging the sphere of their activities.

Let us consider some of the ways in which a knowledge of chemistry has helped man in the past, and may help him in the future.

It was discovered centuries ago that preparations could be made from certain plants, such as poppies and coca, which, when taken by a human being, serve to deaden pain. From these plants chemists isolated pure substances, morphine and cocaine, which have the pain-deadening property. These substances have, however, an undesirable property, that of inducing a craving for them that sometimes leads to drug addiction. Chemists then investigated morphine and cocaine, to learn their chemical structure, and then made, in the laboratory, a great number of other substances, somewhat similar in structure, and tested these substances for their powers of deadening pain and of producing addiction. In this way some drugs that are far more valuable than the natural ones have been discovered; one example is procaine, a local anesthetic used in minor surgery.

A related story is that of the discovery of general anesthetics. A cen tury and a half ago Davy, as a young man just beginning his scientific career, tested many gases on himself by inhaling them. (He was lucky that he did not kill himself, because one of the gases he inhaled is very poisonous.) He discovered that one gas produced a state of hysteria when inhaled, and that people under the influence of this gas, which was given the name laughing gas, seemed not to suffer pain when they fell down or bumped into an object. It is surprising that this observation did not at once suggest to him that laughing gas might beneficially be used in surgical operations. No one seems to have had this idea, however, and the use of anesthetics was delayed for nearly half a century. Then an investigator in the United States noticed that the chemical substance ether, when inhaled, produces unconsciousness, and another noticed the same effect with chloroform. These substances were soon brought into general use for producing unconsciousness during surgical operations. The discovery of anesthesia was a great discovery, not only because it relieves pain, but also because it permits delicate surgical operations to be carried out that would be impossible if the patients remained conscious.

The rubber industry is one that may be mentioned as an example of a chemical industry. This industry began when it was discovered that raw rubber, a sticky material made from the sap of the rubber tree, could be converted into vulcanized rubber, which has superior properties (greatly increased strength, freedom from stickiness), by mixing it with sulfur and heating it. During recent years artificial materials similar to rubber (called synthetic rubber) have been made, which are in many ways better than natural rubber. The synthetic rubbers are made from petroleum.

The steel industry is another great chemical industry. Steel, which consists mainly of the metal iron, is our most important structural material. It is made from iron ore by a complex chemical process. In the United States the production of steel is carried on at the rate of more than 1000 lbs. per person per year.

Chemistry plays such an important part in the life of twentieth-century man that this age may properly be called the chemical age.

1-1. *The Study of Chemistry*

Chemistry has two main aspects: **descriptive chemistry**, *the discovery and tabulation of chemical facts;* and **theoretical chemistry**, *the formulation of theories that, upon verification, unify these facts and combine them into a system.**

---

* The broad field of chemistry may also be divided in other ways. An important division of chemistry is that into the branches *organic chemistry* and *inorganic chemistry*. Organic chemistry is the chemistry of the compounds of carbon, especially those that occur in plants and animals. Inorganic chemistry is the chemistry of the compounds of elements other than carbon. Each of these branches of chemistry is in part descriptive and in part theoretical. Many other

It is not possible to obtain a sound knowledge of chemistry simply by learning theoretical chemistry. Even if a student were to learn all the chemical theory that is known, he would not have a knowledge of the science, because a major part of chemistry (many of the special properties of individual substances) has not yet been well incorporated into chemical theory. It is accordingly necessary for the student to learn a number of the facts of descriptive chemistry simply by memorizing them. The number of these facts that might be memorized is enormous, and increases rapidly year by year, as new discoveries are made. In this book a selection from the more important facts is presented. You should learn some of these facts by studying them, and by frequently referring to them and renewing your knowledge of them. You should also learn as much about chemistry as possible from your own experience in the laboratory and from your observations of chemical substances and chemical reactions in everyday life.

A special effort has been made in this book to present the subject of chemistry in a logical and simple manner, and to correlate descriptive chemistry with the theories of chemistry. It is therefore necessary that the theoretical sections of the book be carefully studied and thoroughly understood. Read each chapter with care. Examine the arguments to be sure that you understand them.

At the beginning of many chapters there is a paragraph telling about the relation of the chapter to the other chapters and to the whole subject of chemistry. At the end, just preceding the problems, there is a list of concepts, facts, and technical terms that will serve as a guide in review of the chapter. Be sure that you understand the new concepts and terms before going on to the next chapter.

1–2. *Matter*

The universe is composed of **matter** *and* **radiant energy.**

The chemist is primarily interested in matter, but he must also study radiant energy—light, x-rays, radio waves—in its interaction with substances. For example, he may be interested in the color of substances, which is produced by their absorption of light.

Matter consists of all the materials around us—gases, liquids, solids. This statement is really not a definition. The dictionary states that matter is "that of which a physical object is composed; material." Then it defines material and physical object as matter, so that we are back where we started. The best course that we can follow is to say that no one really knows how to define matter, but that we agree to start out by using the

---

branches of chemistry, which in general are parts of organic chemistry and inorganic chemistry, have also been given names; for example, analytical chemistry, physical chemistry, biochemistry, nuclear chemistry, industrial chemistry. Their nature is indicated by their names.

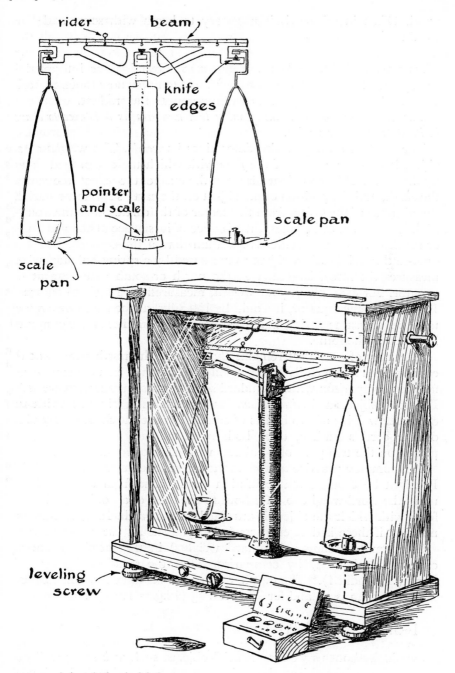

FIGURE 1·1 *A chemical balance.*

word. Often in science it is necessary to begin with some undefined words.

Mass and Weight. All matter has *mass*. Chemists are interested in the masses of materials, because they want to know how much material they need to use to prepare a certain amount of a product.

The **mass** *of an object is the quantity that measures its resistance to change in its state of rest or motion.*

The mass of an object also determines its *weight*. The weight of an object is only a measure of the *force* with which the object is attracted by the earth. This force depends upon the mass of the object, the mass of the earth, and the position of the object on the earth's surface, especially the distance of the object from the center of the earth. Since the earth is slightly flattened at its poles, the distance of its surface at the north pole or south pole from its center is less than that at the equator. In consequence the weight of an object as measured by a spring balance, which measures the force, is greater at the north or south pole than at the equator. For example, if your weight, measured by a spring balance, is 150.0 lbs. at the equator, it would be 150.8 lbs. at the north pole, measured on the same spring balance—nearly a pound more. Your mass, however, is the same.

The mass of an object remains the same at the north pole as at the equator, and it can easily be determined, at any place on the earth's surface, by comparison with a standard set of masses (standard "weights"). For small objects a *chemical balance*, such as shown in Figure 1-1, is used. Since the weights of two bodies of equal mass are the same at any place on the earth's surface, these bodies will balance one another when placed on the two pans of a balance with arms of equal length.

It is common practice to refer to the masses of objects as their weights. It might be thought that confusion would arise from the practice of using the word weight to refer both to the mass of an object and to the force with which the object is attracted by the earth. In general it does not, but if there is danger of confusion you should use the word mass.

The standard masses (standard weights) in the metric system are calibrated (checked) by comparison with the standard kilogram in Paris (Appendix 1).* The metric unit of mass is the *gram*. The abbreviation for gram is g, and for kilogram kg (1 kg = 1000 g).

1-3. *Kinds of Matter*

As we look about us we see material objects, such as a stone wall or a table, or one of the objects shown in Figure 1-2. The chemist is primarily

---

* There are many systems of weights and measures, which are ordinarily used in different countries. In order to avoid confusion, all scientists use the *metric system*, which is described in Appendix 1, in their scientific work. In general, we shall use the metric system in this book, but an occasional exercise or example may be given in the American system.

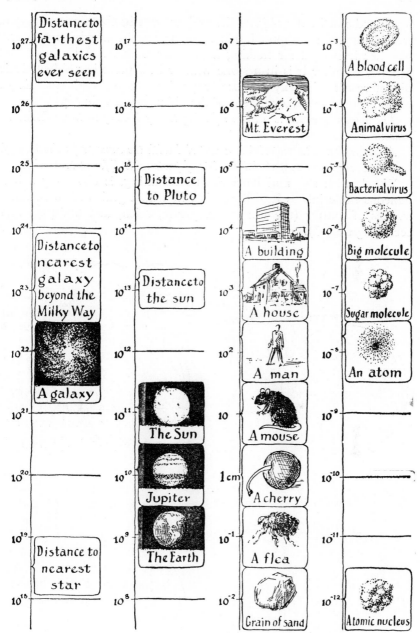

FIGURE 1-2   *A diagram showing dimensions of objects, from 10^{-12} cm (the nucleus of an atom) to 10^{27} cm (the radius of the known universe).*

interested not in the objects themselves, but in the kinds of matter of which they are composed. He is interested in wood, as a material, whether it is used for making a table or a chair. He is interested in granite, whether it is in a stone wall or in some other object. Indeed, his interest is primarily in those properties (characteristic qualities) of a material that are independent of the objects containing it.

The word **material** *is used in referring to any kind of matter, whether homogeneous or heterogeneous.*

A **homogeneous** *material is a material with the same properties throughout.*

A **heterogeneous** *material consists of parts with different properties.*

Wood, with soft and hard rings alternating, is obviously a heterogeneous material, as is also granite, in which grains of three different species of matter (the minerals* quartz, mica, and feldspar) can be seen (Figure 1-3).

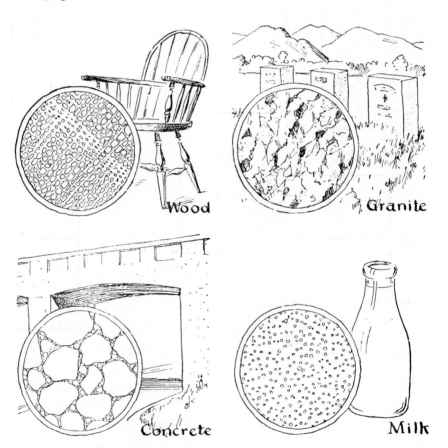

FIGURE 1-3 *Some heterogeneous materials.*

* A *mineral* is any homogeneous material occurring naturally as a product of inorganic processes (that is, not produced by a living organism).

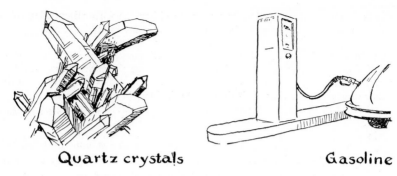

Quartz crystals   **Gasoline**

FIGURE 1-4   *Some homogeneous materials.*

Heterogeneous materials are mixtures of two or more homogeneous materials. For example, each of the three minerals quartz, mica, and feldspar that constitute the rock granite is a homogeneous material (Figure 1-4).

Let is now define the words *substance* and *solution.*

A **substance** *is a homogeneous species of matter with definite chemical composition.*

A **solution** *is a homogeneous material that does not have a definite composition.**

Pure salt, pure sugar, pure iron, pure copper, pure sulfur, pure water, pure oxygen, and pure hydrogen are representative substances. Quartz is also a substance (Figure 1-4).

On the other hand, a solution of sugar in water is not a substance according to this definition: it is, to be sure, homogeneous, but it does not satisfy the second part of the above definition, inasmuch as its composition is not definite, but is widely variable, being determined by the amount of sugar that happens to have been dissolved in a given amount of water. Gasoline is also not a pure substance; it is a solution (a homogeneous mixture) of several substances.

Sometimes the word substance is used in a broader sense, essentially as equivalent to material. Chemists usually restrict the use of the word in the way given by the definition above. The chemist's usage of the word substance may be indicated by using the phrase "pure substance."

Most materials that the chemist classifies as substances (pure substances) have definite chemical composition; for example, all samples of salt contain 39.4% sodium and 60.6% chlorine. Other compounds, however, show a small range of variation of chemical composition; an example is the iron sulfide that is made by heating iron and sulfur together. This homogeneous material when made in different ways shows a range in composition of from 35% to 39% sulfur.

---

* The word solution is commonly used for liquid solutions. Chemists also refer to gaseous solutions (mixtures of two or more pure gases) and to solid solutions.

Kinds of Definition.   Definitions may be either precise or imprecise. The mathematician may define precisely the words that he uses; in his further discussion he then adheres rigorously to the defined meaning of each word. On the other hand, the words that are used in describing nature, which is itself complex, may not be capable of precise definition. In giving a definition for such a word the effort is made to describe the accepted usage.

For example, sometimes it is difficult to decide whether a material is homogeneous (a solution) or is heterogeneous (a mixture). A specimen of granite, in which grains of three different species of matter can be seen, is obviously a mixture. An emulsion of fat in water (a suspension of small droplets of fat in the water, as in milk, Figure 1-3) is also a mixture. The heterogeneity of a piece of granite is obvious to the eye. The heterogeneity of milk can be seen if a drop of milk is examined under a microscope. But if the droplets of fat in the emulsion were made smaller and smaller, it might become impossible to observe the heterogeneity of the material. In such a border-line case the material may be called either a solution or a mixture.

Substances are classified as *elementary substances* or *compounds*.

A substance that can be decomposed into two or more substances is a **compound.**

A substance that cannot be decomposed is an **elementary substance** (*or* **element**).*

Salt can be decomposed by an electric current into two substances, sodium and chlorine. Hence salt is a compound.

Water can be decomposed by an electric current into two substances, hydrogen and oxygen. Hence water is a compound.

Mercuric oxide can be decomposed by heat, to form mercury and oxygen. Hence mercuric oxide is a compound.

No one has ever succeeded in decomposing sodium, chlorine, hydrogen, oxygen, or mercury into other substances. Hence these five substances are accepted as elementary substances (elements).

At the present time (1955) exactly 100 elements are known. Several hundred thousand compounds of these 100 elements have been found in nature or made in the laboratory.

The process of decomposing a compound into two or more simpler substances is sometimes called *analysis*. The reverse process, of forming a substance by combining two or more substances, is called *synthesis*.

The composition of a compound can be determined by analysis. For example, a *qualitative analysis* of salt might be carried out by decomposing it with an electric current and identifying the products as sodium and chlorine; the chemist could then say that the salt is a compound of the two elements sodium and chlorine. To carry out a *quantitative analysis* he would have to weigh the substances; he could then report the composition as 39.4% sodium, 60.6% chlorine.

Our classification of matter is summarized in the following chart. You may find it worth while to examine this chart carefully. Can you define all of the words? Can you give two or three examples of each of the six

---

* The discovery of radioactivity made it necessary to change these definitions slightly (see the last section of Chapter 4).

kinds of materials that might constitute an object? Can you think of one or two materials that are hard to classify?

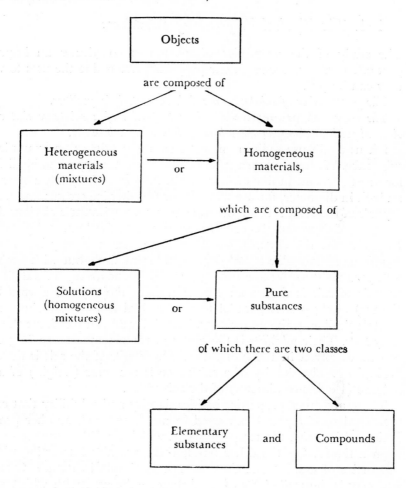

Illustrative Exercises

1-1. Is ice an elementary substance or a compound?

1-2. Is maple syrup (or corn syrup) a homogeneous material or a heterogeneous material? Is it a solution or a substance (pure substance)?

1-3. Sterling silver is a homogeneous material made by melting silver and copper together. In Great Britain its composition is 92.5% silver, 7.5% copper, and in the United States it is 90% silver, 10% copper (coinage silver). Any intermediate composition may be used, and will give a homogeneous material. Is sterling silver a compound, or is it a solid solution?

1-4. When the substance calcite is heated it forms lime and carbon dioxide. Is calcite an elementary substance or a compound? Can you say whether or not lime is an elementary substance or a compound?

1-5. When diamond is heated in a vacuum (no other material present) it is converted completely into graphite. Does this prove that diamond is a compound?

1–4. *The Physical Properties of Substances*

The study of the properties of substances constitutes an important part of chemistry, because their properties determine the uses to which they can be put.

The **properties** *of substances are their characteristic qualities.*

The **physical properties** *are those properties of a substance that can be observed without changing the substance into other substances.*

Let us again use sodium chloride, common salt, as an example of a substance. We have all seen this substance in what appear to be different forms—table salt, in fine grains; salt in the form of crystals a quarter of an inch in diameter, for use with ice for freezing ice cream; and natural crystals of rock salt an inch or more across. Despite their obvious difference, all of these samples of salt have the same fundamental properties. In each case the crystals, small or large, are naturally bounded by square or rectangular *crystal faces* of different sizes, but with each face always at right angles to each adjacent face. The *cleavage* of the different crystals of salt is the same: when crushed, the crystals always break (cleave) along planes parallel to the original faces, producing smaller crystals similar to the larger ones. The different samples have the same salty *taste*. Their *solubility* is the same: at room temperature 36 g of salt can be dissolved in 100 g of water. The *density* of the salt is the same, 2.16 g/cm^3. The density of a substance is the mass (weight) of a unit volume (1 cubic centimeter) of the substance.

There are other properties besides density and solubility that can be measured precisely and expressed in numbers. Such another property is the *melting point*, the temperature at which a solid substance melts to form a liquid. On the other hand, there are also interesting physical properties of a substance that are not so simple in nature. One such property is the *malleability* of a substance—the ease with which a substance can be hammered out into thin sheets. A related property is the *ductility*—the ease with which the substance can be drawn into a wire. *Hardness* is a similar property: we say that one substance is less hard than the second substance when it is scratched by the second substance. The *color* of a substance is an important physical property.

It is customary to say that under the same external conditions all specimens of a particular substance have the same physical properties (density, hardness, color, melting point, crystalline form, etc.). Sometimes, however, the word substance is used in referring to a material without regard to its state. For example, ice, liquid water, and water vapor may be referred to as the same substance. Moreover, a specimen containing crystals of rock salt and crystals of table salt may be called a mixture, even though the specimen may consist entirely of one substance, sodium chloride. This lack of definiteness in usage seems to cause no confusion in practice.

The concept "pure substance" is, of course, an idealization; all actual substances are more or less impure. It is a useful concept, however, because we have learned through experiment that the properties of various specimens of an impure substance with different impurities are nearly the same if the impurities are present in only small amounts. These properties are accepted as the properties of the ideal substance.

1–5. *The Chemical Properties of Substances*

The **chemical properties** *of a substance are those properties that relate to its participation in chemical reactions.*

Chemical reactions *are the processes that convert substances into other substances.*

Thus sodium chloride has the property of changing into a soft metal, sodium, and a greenish-yellow gas, chlorine, when it is decomposed by passage of an electric current through it. It also has the property, when it is dissolved in water, of producing a white precipitate when a solution of silver nitrate is added to it; and it has many other chemical properties.

Iron has the property of combining readily with the oxygen in moist air, to form iron rust; whereas an alloy* of iron with chromium and nickel (stainless steel) is found to resist this process of rusting. It is evident from this example that the chemical properties of materials are important in engineering.

Many chemical reactions take place in the kitchen. When biscuits are made with use of sour milk and baking soda there is a chemical reaction between the baking soda and a substance in the sour milk, lactic acid, to produce the gas carbon dioxide, which leavens the dough by forming small bubbles in it. And, of course, a great many chemical reactions take place in the human body. Foods that we eat are digested in the stomach and intestines. Oxygen in the inhaled air combines with a substance, hemoglobin, in the red cells of the blood, and then is released in the tissues, where it takes part in many different reactions. Many biochemists and physiologists are engaged in the study of the chemical reactions that take place in the human body.

Most substances have the power to enter into many chemical reactions. The study of these reactions constitutes a large part of the study of chemistry. Chemistry may be defined as *the science of substances—their structure, their properties, and the reactions that change them into other substances.*

---

* An *alloy* is a metallic material containing two or more elements. It may be either homogeneous or heterogeneous (a mixture of grains of two or more kinds). If homogeneous, it may be either a pure compound or a solid solution, or even a liquid solution—many alloys of mercury and other metals are liquid.

Illustrative Exercises

1-6.   Which of the following processes would you class as chemical reactions?
       (a) The boiling of water.
       (b) The burning of paper.
       (c) The preparation of sugar syrup by adding sugar to hot water.
       (d) The formation of rust on iron.
       (e) The manufacture of salt by evaporation of sea water.

1-7.   A kilogram of gold (2.2 lbs.) occupies the volume 51.5 cubic centimeters. What is
       the density of gold? (Ans. 19.4 g/cm³.)
       If the gold were in the form of a cube, what would be the length of its edge? Find
       the answer in centimeters, and also in inches.

1–6. *Energy and Temperature*

The concept of *energy* is as difficult to define as that of matter. Energy is
involved in doing work, or in heating an object. A boulder at the top of
a mountain has *potential energy*. As it rolls down the mountain side, its
potential energy is changed into the *kinetic energy* of its motion. If it were
to fall into a lake, and be slowed down by the friction of its motion
through water, part of its kinetic energy would be changed by friction
into *heat*, which then would raise the temperature of the boulder and
of the water. In addition, part of its kinetic energy would be transferred
to the water, and would evidence itself in waves radiating from the point
of impact.

Another important kind of energy is *radiant energy*. Visible light,
infrared radiation, ultraviolet radiation, x-rays, and radio waves are
radiant energy. They are all closely similar in nature (see Section 28–5).

When a mixture of gasoline vapor and air is exploded, energy is liberated—energy which can do the work of propelling an automobile, and
which in addition causes an increase in temperature of the engine and
the exhaust gases. This energy is said to have been stored up in the gasoline and air as *chemical energy*.

The Law of Conservation of Energy.   It has been found that *whenever energy of one form disappears an equivalent amount of energy of other forms
is produced*. This principle is called the **law of conservation of energy.**

All chemical reactions are accompanied by either the liberation of
energy or the absorption of energy. Usually this energy is in the form
of heat. If some substances when mixed together in a flask undergo a
chemical reaction with liberation of heat, the contents of the flask become warmer. If, on the other hand, they undergo a chemical reaction
with absorption of heat, the contents of the flask become colder. These
facts can be described by saying that every substance has a certain *heat
content*, and that in general the heat contents of the products of a reaction
differ from the heat contents of the reactants. In accordance with the

law of conservation of energy, the *heat of the reaction* is the difference in heat contents of the products and the reactants. For example, a mixture of gasoline and oxygen has a greater total heat content than the products of their reaction, which are carbon dioxide and water. In consequence, some heat is liberated during the reaction.

Under some conditions chemical energy is liberated during a chemical reaction in forms other than heat. For example, the chemical energy stored up in an explosive may do work, in breaking a stone cliff into fragments. The chemical energy in the substances of an electric battery is converted into electric energy during the operation of the battery. Some of the chemical energy in a fuel may be converted into radiant energy as the fuel burns.

Temperature.   If two objects are placed in contact with one another, heat may flow from one object to the other one. *Temperature* is the quality that determines the direction in which heat flows—it always flows from the object at higher temperature to the object at lower temperature.

Temperatures are ordinarily measured by means of a thermometer, such as the ordinary mercury thermometer, consisting of a quantity of mercury in a glass tube. The temperature scale used by scientists is the *centigrade scale* or *Celsius scale;* it was introduced by Anders Celsius, a Swedish professor of astronomy, in 1742. On this scale the temperature of freezing water is 0° C, and the temperature of boiling water is 100° C.

On the *Fahrenheit scale*, used in every-day life in English-speaking countries, the freezing point of water is 32° F, and the boiling point of water is 212° F. On this scale the

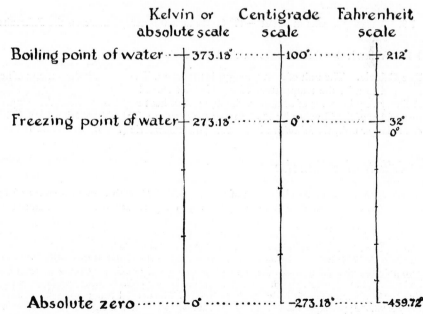

FIGURE 1-5   *Comparison of Kelvin, Centigrade, and Fahrenheit scales of temperature.*

freezing point and the boiling point differ by 180°, rather than the 100° of the centigrade scale.*

The relation between the centigrade scale and the Fahrenheit scale is indicated in Figure 1-5. To convert temperatures from one scale to another, you need only remember that the Fahrenheit degree is $\frac{100}{180}$ or $\frac{5}{9}$ of the centigrade degree, and that 0° C is the same temperature as 32° F.

Example 1. A school room may be kept at 68° F. What is this temperature on the centigrade scale?

  Solution. 68° F is 36° F (that is, 68° − 32°) above the freezing point of water. This number of Fahrenheit degrees is equal to $\frac{5}{9} \times 36 = 20°$ C. Since the freezing point of water is 0° C, the temperature of the room is 20° C.

The Absolute Temperature Scale. About one hundred fifty years ago it was noticed by scientists that a sample of gas that is cooled decreases in volume in a regular way, and it was seen that if the volume were to continue to decrease in the same way it would become zero at about −273° C. The concept was developed that this temperature, −273° C (more accurately, −273.16° C), is the minimum temperature, the *absolute zero*. A new temperature scale was then devised by Lord Kelvin, a great British physicist (1824–1907). It is called either the *absolute temperature scale* (A) or the *Kelvin scale* (K). The unit on this scale is the centigrade degree. † In order to convert a temperature from the centigrade scale to the absolute scale, it is only necessary to add 273.16°. Thus the freezing point of water, 0° C, is 273.16° K. The relation of the Kelvin scale to the centigrade scale and the Fahrenheit scale is also shown in Figure 1-5.

Illustrative Exercises

 1-8. The normal temperature of the human body is 98.6° F. What is it on the centigrade scale?

 1-9. Mercury freezes at about −40° C. What is this temperature on the Fahrenheit scale?

 1-10. What is the absolute zero on the Fahrenheit scale?

The Calorie. The unit of heat (energy) is the *calorie*. The calorie is the amount of heat required to raise the temperature of 1 g of water from 14.5° to 15.5° C; or, to within ordinary requirements of accuracy, the amount of heat required to raise the temperature of 1 g of liquid water by 1° C, at any temperature. The abbreviation for calorie is cal. A larger unit, the *kilocalorie*, is also used; one kilocalorie (1 kcal) is equal to 1000 cal.

Illustrative Exercise

 1-11. Into a flask containing 100 g of water at 20.0° C, with a small amount of acid dissolved in it, there was poured 100 g of water, also at 20.0° C, containing a

---

 * The Fahrenheit scale was devised by Gabriel Daniel Fahrenheit (1686–1736), a natural philosopher who was born in Danzig and settled in Holland. He invented the mercury thermometer in 1714; before then alcohol had been used as the liquid in thermometers. As the zero point on his scale he took the temperature produced by mixing equal quantities of snow and ammonium chloride. His choice of 212° for the boiling point of water was made in order that the temperature of his body should be 100° F. The normal temperature of the human body is 98.6° F; perhaps Fahrenheit had a slight fever while he was calibrating his thermometer.

 † Another absolute scale, the *Rankine scale*, is sometimes used in engineering work in the English-speaking countries. It uses the Fahrenheit degree, and has 0° R at the absolute zero.

small amount of sodium hydroxide. The temperature of the mixed solution increased to 24.5° C. Neglecting the effect of the substances dissolved in the water and the loss of heat to the flask, calculate how much heat (how many calories) was produced by the reaction of the acid and the sodium hydroxide.

1-7. *Pressure*

In chemical work it is often necessary to know not only the temperature at which an experiment is carried out, but also the *pressure*. For example, the large-scale industrial preparation of ammonia is carried out at high pressure, because the chemical reaction does not proceed satisfactorily at ordinary pressure.

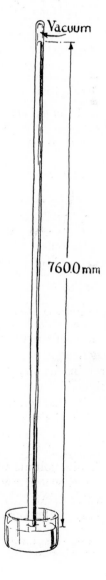

Vacuum

760.0 mm

FIGURE 1-6

A simple mercury barometer.

Pressure is force per unit area. Pressure may be measured in grams per square centimeter, or in pounds per square inch, or in other units. The atmosphere of the earth exerts a pressure on all objects at the surface of the earth. The pressure of the atmosphere is 14.7 pounds per square inch.

Another unit of pressure that is often used is the *atmosphere* (abbreviation atm). The pressure 1 atm is the average pressure at the surface of the earth (at sea level) that is due to the weight of the air.

The pressure due to the atmosphere can be measured by means of a *barometer*. A simple barometer is shown in Figure 1-6. This barometer is made by filling a long glass tube, which is closed at one end, with mercury, being careful that no air remains entrapped, and then inverting the open end of the tube under the surface of some mercury in a cup. If the tube is longer than 760 millimeters (76 cm, about 29.9 inches) the surface of the mercury at the upper end of the tube drops, until the height of the mercury column, measured from the level of mercury in the cup, is just enough to balance the atmospheric pressure. This occurs when the weight of the column of mercury, per unit area, is equal to the pressure of the atmosphere.

Pressure is often reported as the height of the column of mercury required to balance it. For example, the pressure 1 atm is equal to 760 millimeters of mercury (abbreviated as mm of mercury, or mm Hg).

The units used to measure pressure are summarized in the following equation:

$$1 \text{ atm} = 760 \text{ mm Hg} = 14.7 \text{ pounds per square inch}*$$

Illustrative Exercises

1·12. Pressure can also be reported in grams per square centimeter. The density of mercury is 13.55 g/cm³. What is 1 atm pressure in g/cm²? (Remember that 1 atm = 76 cm Hg.)

1·13. The density of water is about 1 g/cm³. At what depth would a diver have to descend under the surface of a lake in order that the pressure acting on him would be 2 atm, rather than the 1 atm that is due to the weight of the air? What is this depth in feet? (Remember that 1 inch equals 2.54 cm. You may want to use the answer to the preceding exercise to solve this one.)

1–8. Solids, Liquids, and Gases

Materials may exist as solids, liquids, or gases. A specimen of a solid, such as a piece of ice, has a definite volume and also has rigidity. It retains its shape, even when acted on by an outside force, provided that the force is not great enough to break or to deform the specimen. A liquid, such as a portion of water in a cup, has a definite volume, but adjusts its shape to the shape of the bottom part of its container. A gas, such as steam (water vapor) in the cylinder of a steam engine, has neither definite shape nor definite volume—it changes its shape and also its volume with change in the shape and volume of the container.

Ice, water, and water vapor represent the same chemical substance, water substance, in three different states. Ice is the *solid state* (*crystalline state*), water the *liquid state*, and water vapor the *gaseous state*.

---

* Engineers use the abbreviation psi for pounds per square inch.

Scientists usually distinguished between *crystalline solids* and *non-crystalline solids*.

A **crystal** *is a homogeneous material* (either a pure substance or a solution) *that, as a result of its regular internal structure, has spontaneously assumed the shape of a figure bounded by plane faces*.

For example, when a solution of salt evaporates small cubes of solid salt form. These cubes, which are bounded by plane square faces, are crystals.

Most solid substances are crystalline in nature. Sometimes the individual crystals, with plane faces and sharp edges and corners, are visible to the naked eye, and sometimes they can be seen only under a microscope.

Some solids, such as charcoal, do not show any crystalline character even when examined with a microscope of high power; these solids are called *amorphous solids* (the word amorphous means without shape).

Certain other materials, of which sealing wax is an example, are called *super-cooled liquids*. When a stick of sealing wax, which is hard and brittle at room temperature, is gradually warmed it begins to soften, and finally becomes a mobile liquid. As it is being cooled it shows a gradual change from a mobile liquid to a viscous liquid, and then to a solid. Even at room temperature it might be described as a liquid which is so viscous that it flows only extremely slowly.

1-9. *The Scientific Method*

During your study of chemistry you will also learn something about the *scientific method*.

Scientists do their work in many ways. A great scientific discovery is often the result of a great flight of the imagination—a brilliant new idea. If you have studied physics, you probably read that Archimedes is said to have been taking a bath when he had his brilliant idea, a "flash of genius," about the change in weight of a body immersed in a liquid (Archimedes' principle). Curiosity and an active imagination are great assets to a scientist.

No one knows the method for having brilliant new ideas, and this is not part of what is ordinarily called the scientific method. But scientists also work by applying common sense, reliable methods of reasoning, to the problems that they are attacking, and the procedure that they follow, which is called the scientific method, can be learned.

Part of the scientific method is the requirement that the investigator be willing to accept all of the facts. He must not be prejudiced; prejudice might keep him from giving proper consideration to some of the facts, or to some of the logical arguments involved in applying the scientific method, and in this way keep him from getting the right answer. If you were to say "I have made up my mind—don't confuse me with a lot of facts," you would not be applying the scientific method.

The remaining part of the scientific method consists of logical argument.

The first step in applying the scientific method is to obtain some facts, by observation and experiment. The next step is to classify and correlate the facts by general statements. If a general statement is simple in form it may be called a *law of nature*. If it is more complex it is called a *theory*. Both laws of nature and theories are called *principles*.

The discussion of the scientific method will be continued in the first section of the following chapter.

1–10. *How to Study Chemistry*

You may feel, now that you are just beginning your formal study of chemistry, that you know nothing about this subject; *but in fact you already know a great deal*—many things that the foremost scientists did not know a century or two ago. From your general reading, from the comic papers, the advertisements, and your contact with automobiles, street signs, and other features of our modern world, you probably know that not only oxygen, hydrogen, iron, and copper are elements, but also that helium, neon, and argon are elements, and that they are gases; that copper, zinc, tin, and lead are elements, and are metals; and that sulfur, phosphorus, and bromine are elements that are non-metals. In addition to knowing that water and sodium chloride are compounds, you know that penicillin is a compound used for the treatment of infectious diseases. You know that substances are composed of atoms, and that the atoms themselves consist of nuclei and electrons. You probably even know, from reading the newspapers, that neutrons can cause the nuclei of atoms of uranium 235 and plutonium 239 to split—to undergo fission during the detonation of an atomic bomb; this is knowledge that was possessed by nobody in the world a few years ago.

By studying chemistry you can make the understanding that you have of the nature of the universe more precise, and you can add greatly to it.

It was mentioned in Section 1–1 that part of the study of chemistry consists in memorizing some of the facts of descriptive chemistry. If you are planning to become a chemist, or a scientist or professional man or woman in a field in which chemistry is important, you should try to learn a large number of the facts of descriptive chemistry. If your reason for studying chemistry is not a professional one, you may not want to learn so many of these facts, but only some of them, especially those that are significant to everyday life.

In applying a theoretical principle in the solution of a problem, you should make use of the following procedure. First, decide on the applicable principle and get it clearly in mind. Then apply it in a straightforward manner. *Do not guess:* if you are not sure of the proper step, think about the matter further, until you are sure.

In working problems you must be sure that you understand the theoretical principle that you are using before making the calculations. It is important to keep track of the physical units that are involved in the problem. One good way of doing this is to write the abbreviations for the units beside the numbers, and to cancel them when possible. For example, if you are told that 1.73 g of a substance occupies the volume 2.00 cm³, and are asked to calculate the density, you may write 1.73 g/2.00 cm³, and obtain immediately the answer 0.865 g/cm³. The fact that the answer is in units g/cm³ gives you a check on the correctness of the procedure that you have followed, inasmuch as you know that density is measured in units g/cm³.

Concepts and Terms Introduced in This Chapter

Chemistry—the study of substances, their structure, their properties, and their reactions.

Descriptive chemistry—the discovery and tabulation of chemical facts.

Theoretical chemistry—the formulation of theories that unify these facts and combine them into a system.

Matter—the gases, liquids, and solids that, with radiant energy, make up the universe.

Radiant energy—light, x-rays, radio waves.

Mass—the quantity that measures the resistance to change in state of motion of an object.

Weight—the force with which an object is attracted by the earth.

Material—any kind of matter.

Homogeneous material—material with the same properties throughout.

Heterogeneous material—material consisting of parts with different properties.

Mineral—any homogeneous material occurring naturally as a product of inorganic processes.

Substance—a homogeneous species of matter with definite chemical composition.

Solution—a homogeneous material that does not have a definite composition.

Compound—a substance that can be decomposed into two or more substances.

Elementary substance or element—a substance that cannot be decomposed.

Properties of substances—their characteristic qualities.

Physical properties—those properties not connected with participation in chemical reactions. Examples: formation of crystal faces, cleavage, taste, solubility, density, melting point, malleability, ductility, hardness, color.

Chemical properties—those properties that relate to participation of a substance in chemical reactions.

Chemical reactions—the processes that convert substances into other substances.

Alloy—a metallic material containing two or more elements.

Forms of energy—potential energy, kinetic energy, heat, radiant energy, chemical energy.

Law of conservation of energy—in all ordinary changes energy of one forms disappears at the same time that an equivalent amount of energy of other forms is produced.

Temperature—the quality that determines the direction in which heat flows.

Calorie—the unit of heat, the amount of heat required to raise the temperature of 1 g of water by 1° C.

Temperature scales—centigrade scale (Celsius scale); Fahrenheit scale; Kelvin scale (absolute temperature scale).

Pressure—force per unit area. Units of pressure: atm, mm Hg, pounds per square inch, g/cm^3.

Solids, liquids, gases. The crystalline state. Crystal—a homogeneous material that has spontaneously assumed the shape of a figure bounded by plane faces. Amorphous solids. Supercooled liquids.

The scientific method: willingness to accept all of the facts; freedom from prejudice; logical argument; classification and correlation of facts by use of general statements.

Exercises

1-14.   A cube of gold 2 cm on edge weighs 155.4 g. What is the density of gold?

1-15.   Classify the following materials as homogeneous or heterogeneous:

pure gold	air	glass
milk	ice	sugar
wood	gasoline	coffee

1-16.   Is the ice in a glacier to be classified, according to the definition of mineral, as a mineral?

1-17.   Classify the following homogeneous materials as substances or solutions:

rain water	ocean water	oxygen
air	gasoline	mercury
sterling silver	salt	honey

1-18.   What is the evidence proving that water is a compound, and not an element? What is the evidence indicating that oxygen is an element, and not a compound? Why is the word "proving" used in the first of the preceding sentences, and "indicating" in the second?

1-19.   How much heat is needed to raise the temperature of 200 g of water from 10° C to 50° C?

1-20.   The melting point of pure iron is 1535° C. What is this temperature on the Fahrenheit scale?

Reference Books

Further information about descriptive chemistry may be obtained from textbooks and treatises such as the following:

M. C. Sneed and J. L. Maynard, *General Inorganic Chemistry*, D. Van Nostrand Co., New York, 1942.

F. Ephraim, *Inorganic Chemistry*, Interscience Publishers, Inc., New York, 1954.

J. H. Hildebrand and R. E. Powell, *Principles of Chemistry*, The Macmillan Co., New York, 1952.

W. M. Latimer and J. H. Hildebrand, *Reference Book of Inorganic Chemistry*, The Macmillan Co., New York, **1951**.

Much useful information is tabulated in the following handbooks. It is suggested that the student majoring in chemistry obtain a copy of one of them:

Charles D. Hodgman (Editor-in-Chief), *Handbook of Chemistry and Physics*, Chemical Rubber Publishing Co., Cleveland, Ohio.

N. A. Lange, *Handbook of Chemistry*, Handbook Publishers, Sandusky, Ohio.

Detailed information about the elements and inorganic compounds may be found in comprehensive treatises; the greatest of these in English is

J. W. Mellor, *A Comprehensive Treatise on Inorganic and Theoretical Chemistry*, Longmans, Green and Co., New York, **1922–1937**.

You may read about the history of chemistry in the following books:

Alexander Findlay, *One Hundred Years of Chemistry*, The Macmillan Co., New York, **1948**.

Mary E. Weeks, *Discovery of the Elements*, Journal of Chemical Education, Easton, Pa., **1945**.

H. N. Smith, *Torchbearers of Chemistry*, Academic Press, New York, **1949**.

Bernard Jaffe, *Crucibles: The Story of Chemistry from Ancient Alchemy to Nuclear Fission*, Simon and Schuster, New York, **1948**.

F. J. Moore (revised by W. T. Hall), *A History of Chemistry*, McGraw-Hill Book Co., New York, 1939.

James B. Conant, *On Understanding Science: An Historical Approach*, Yale University Press, New Haven, Conn., **1948**.

For the chemistry of stars, planets, comets, interstellar space, etc., see

R. H. Baker, *Astronomy*, D. Van Nostrand Co., New York, **1950**.

Many interesting articles may be found in the *Journal of Chemical Education* and in the *Scientific American*. The chemical articles in the *Encyclopaedia Britannica* are excellent.

Chapter 2

The Atomic
Structure of Matter

The properties of any kind of matter are most easily and clearly learned and understood when they are correlated with its structure, in terms of the molecules, atoms, and still smaller particles that compose it. This subject, the atomic theory of matter, will be taken up in this chapter.

The chapter begins with a brief discussion of hypotheses, theories, and laws (Section 2–1). The next section (2–2) describes the atomic theory of matter and presents the arguments advanced by Dalton in support of the theory a century and a half ago. A brief discussion of modern methods of studying atoms and molecules follows (Section 2–3). There are then described, as examples, a crystal of copper, built of atoms in a simple regular arrangement (Section 2–4), and a crystal of iodine, built of molecules (groups of atoms, Section 2–5). Some photographs of molecules made with the electron microscope are also shown in Section 2–5. Section 2–6 presents a brief description of the classification of crystals into systems. The nature of gases and liquids and the processes of evaporation and sublimation are treated in Sections 2–7 and 2–8, and the relation between temperature and the motion of molecules is discussed in Section 2–9. All of these aspects of atomic and molecular theory are important for the further study of chemistry.

2–1. *Hypotheses, Theories, and Laws*

When it is first found that an idea explains or correlates a number of facts, the idea is called a *hypothesis*. A hypothesis may be subjected to further tests and experimental checking of deductions that may be made from it. If it continues to agree with the results of experiment, the hypothesis is dignified by the name of *theory* or *law*.

A theory, such as the atomic theory, usually involves some idea about the nature of some part of the universe, whereas a law may represent a summarizing statement about observed experimental facts. For example, there is a law of the constancy of the angles between the faces of crystals. This law states that whenever the angles between corresponding faces of various crystals of a pure substance are measured, they are found to have the same value. The law simply expresses the fact that the angles between corresponding faces on a crystal of a pure substance are found to have the same value whether the crystal is a small one or a large one; it does not in any way explain this fact. An explanation of the fact is given by the atomic theory of crystals, the theory that in crystals the atoms are arranged in a regular order (as described later in this chapter).

It may be mentioned that chemists and other scientists use the word theory in two somewhat different senses. The first meaning of the word is that described above, namely, a hypothesis which has been verified. The second use of the word theory is to represent a systematic body of knowledge, compounded of facts, laws, theories in the limited sense described above, deductive arguments, etc. Thus by the atomic theory we mean not only the idea that substances are composed of atoms, but also all the facts about substances that can be explained and interpreted in terms of atoms, and the arguments that have been developed to explain the properties of substances in terms of their atomic structure.

2–2. *The Atomic Theory*

The most important of all chemical theories is the atomic theory. In 1805 the English chemist and physicist John Dalton (1766–1844), of Manchester, stated the hypothesis that *all substances consist of small particles of matter, of several different kinds, corresponding to the different elements.* He called these particles atoms, from the Greek word *atomos*, meaning indivisible. This hypothesis gave a simple explanation or picture of previously observed but unsatisfactorily explained relations among the weights of substances taking part in chemical reactions with one another. As it was verified by further work in chemistry and physics, Dalton's atomic hypothesis became the atomic theory. The existence of atoms is now accepted as a fact.

The rapid progress of our science during the current century is well illustrated by the increase in our knowledge about atoms. In a popular textbook of chemistry written in the early years of the twentieth century atoms were defined as the "imaginary units of which bodies are aggregates." Now, only half a century later, we have precise knowledge of many properties of atoms and molecules. Atoms and molecules can no longer be considered "imaginary."

Dalton's Arguments in Support of the Atomic Theory.   The concept of atoms is very old. The Greek philosopher Democritus (about 460–370 B.C.), who had adopted some of his ideas from earlier philosophers, stated that the universe is composed of void (vacuum) and atoms. The atoms were considered to be everlasting and indivisible— absolutely small, so small that their size could not be diminished. He considered the atoms of different substances, such as water and iron, to be fundamentally the same, but to differ in some superficial way; atoms of water, being smooth and round, could roll over one another, whereas atoms of iron, being rough and jagged, would cling together to form a solid body.

The atomic theory of Democritus was pure speculation, and was much too general to be useful. Dalton's atomic theory, however, was a hypothesis which explained many facts in a simple and reasonable way.

In 1785 the French chemist Antoine Laurent Lavoisier (1743–1794) showed clearly that there is no change in mass during a chemical reaction—the mass of the products is equal to the mass of the reacting substances. This general statement is called the **law of conservation of mass.**

In 1799 another general law, the **law of constant proportions,** was enunciated by the French chemist Joseph Louis Proust (1754–1826). The law of constant proportions states that *different samples of a substance contain its elementary constituents (elements) in the same proportions.* For example, it was found by analysis that the two elements hydrogen and oxygen are present in any sample of water in the proportion by weight 1 : 8. One gram of hydrogen and 8 grams of oxygen combine to form 9 grams of water.

Dalton stated the hypothesis that elements consist of atoms, all of the atoms of one element being identical, and that compounds result from the combination of a certain number of atoms of one element with a certain number of atoms of another element (or, in general, from the combination of atoms of two or more elements, each in definite number). In this way he could give a simple explanation of the law of conservation of mass, and also of the law of constant proportions.

A molecule is a group of atoms bonded to one another.   If a molecule of water is formed by the combination of two atoms of hydrogen with one atom of oxygen, the mass of the molecule would be the sum of the masses of two atoms of hydrogen and an atom of

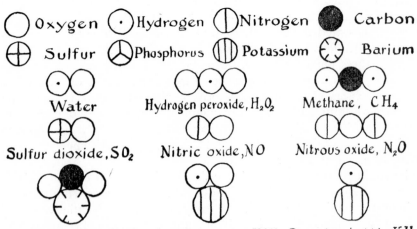

FIGURE 2-1   *Atomic symbols and molecular formulas used by John Dalton, about 1803.*

oxygen, in accordance with the law of conservation of mass. The definite composition of a compound is then explained by the definite ratio of atoms of different elements in the molecules of the compound.

Dalton also formulated another law, the **law of simple multiple proportions.*** This law states that *when two elements combine to form more than one compound, the weights of one element which combine with the same weight of the other are in the ratios of small integers.* It is found by experiment that, whereas water consists of hydrogen and oxygen in the weight ratio 1 : 8, hydrogen peroxide consists of hydrogen and oxygen in the ratio 1 : 16. The weights of oxygen combined with the same weight of hydrogen, one gram, in water and hydrogen peroxide are 8 g and 16 g; that is, they are in the ratio of the small integers 1 and 2. This ratio can be explained by assuming that twice as many atoms of oxygen combine with an atom of hydrogen in hydrogen peroxide as in water. This situation is illustrated in Figure 2-1, which shows the symbols used by Dalton to represent the atoms of some elements and the molecules of compounds.

Dalton had no way of determining the correct formulas of compounds, and he arbitrarily chose formulas to be as simple as possible: for example, he assumed that the molecule of water consisted of one atom of hydrogen and one atom of oxygen, as shown in the figure, whereas in fact it consists of two atoms of hydrogen and one of oxygen.

Illustrative Exercises

2-1. The molecule of sulfur dioxide contains one atom of sulfur and two atoms of oxygen. Sulfur dioxide is 50% sulfur and 50% oxygen by weight. What can you say about the relative weights of atoms of sulfur and oxygen?

2-2. Carbon monoxide is found on chemical analysis to contain 43% carbon and 57% oxygen. Carbon dioxide is found to contain 27% carbon and 73% oxygen. Show that these numbers are compatible with the law of simple multiple proportions.

2-3. Modern Methods of Studying Atoms and Molecules

During the second half of the nineteenth century chemists began to discuss the properties of substances in terms of assumed structures of the molecules—that is, of definite arrangements of the atoms relative to one another. Precise information about the atomic structure of molecules and crystals of many substances was finally obtained during the recent period, beginning about 1920. The physicists have developed many powerful methods of investigating the structure of matter. One of these methods is the interpretation of the *spectra* of substances (see Figure 28-1). A flame containing water vapor, for example, emits light that is characteristic of the water molecule; this is called the spectrum of water vapor. Measurements of the lines in the water spectrum have been made and interpreted, and it has been found that the two hydrogen atoms in the molecule are about 0.97 Å from the oxygen atom.† Moreover, it has been shown that the two hydrogen atoms are not on opposite sides of the oxygen atom, but that the molecule is bent, the angle formed by the three atoms being 106°. The distances between atoms and the angles formed by the atoms in many simple molecules have been determined by spectroscopic methods.

* The discovery of the law of simple multiple proportions was the first great success of Dalton's atomic theory. This law was not induced from experimental results, but was derived from the theory, and then tested by experiments.

† The Ångström (symbol Å), the unit of length used in describing atoms and molecules, is 1×10^{-8} cm. This very small unit of length is convenient because atoms are usually from 1 Å to 3 Å from neighboring atoms in a molecule or crystal, and it is easier to write 0.97 Å than 0.97×10^{-8} cm or 0.0000000097 cm. It was named in honor of a Swedish physicist, Anders Jonas Ångström (1814–1874).

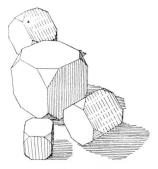

FIGURE 2-2

Crystals of native copper.

Also, the structures of many substances have been determined by the method of diffraction of electrons or diffraction of x-rays. These methods are too complex to be described in this book; you may be interested to read about them in one of the reference books or journals listed at the end of the chapter. In the following pages we shall describe many atomic structures that have been determined by these methods.

2–4. *The Arrangement of Atoms in a Crystal*

Most solid substances are crystalline in nature. Sometimes the particles of a sample of solid substance are themselves single crystals, such as the cubic crystals of sodium chloride in table salt. Sometimes these single crystals are very large; occasionally crystals of minerals several yards in diameter are found in nature.

In our discussion we shall use *copper* as an example. Crystals of copper as large as a centimeter on edge, as shown in Figure 2-2, are found in deposits of copper ore. An ordinary piece of the metal copper does not consist of a single crystal of copper, but of an aggregate of crystals. The crystal grains of a specimen of a metal can be made clearly visible by polishing the surface of the metal, and then etching the metal lightly with an acid. Often the grains are very small, and can be seen only with the aid of a microscope (Figure 2-3), but sometimes they are large, and can be easily seen with the naked eye, as in some brass doorknobs.

FIGURE 2-3

A polished and etched surface of a piece of cold-drawn copper bar, showing the small crystal grains which compose the ordinary metal. Magnification 200 × (200-fold linearly). The small round spots are gas bubbles. (From Dr. S. Kyropoulos.)

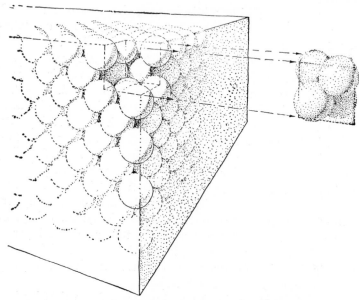

FIGURE 2-4 *The arrangement of atoms in a crystal of copper. The small cube, containing four copper atoms, is the unit of structure; by repeating it the entire crystal is obtained.*

It has been found by experiment* that *every crystal consists of atoms arranged in a three-dimensional pattern which repeats itself regularly.* In a crystal of copper all of the atoms are alike, and they are arranged in the way shown in Figures 2-4 and 2-5. This is a way in which spheres of uniform size may be packed together to occupy the smallest volume.

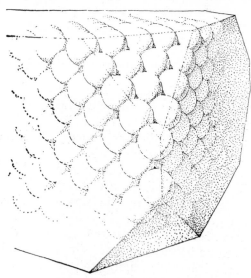

FIGURE 2-5

Another atomic view of a copper crystal, showing small octahedral faces and large cube faces.

* By x-ray diffraction.

You must remember while looking at Figures 2-4 and 2-5 that the atoms are shown greatly enlarged relative to the crystal. Even if the crystal were a small one, with edges only about 0.1 mm long, there would still be about 400,000 atoms in a row along each edge.

It is the **regularity of arrangement** *of the atoms in a crystal which gives to the crystal its characteristic properties, in particular the property of growing in the form of polyhedra.* (A polyhedron is a solid figure bounded by plane faces.) The faces of crystals are defined by surface layers of atoms, as shown in Figures 2-4 and 2-5. These faces lie at angles to one another which have definite characteristic values, the same for all specimens of the same substance. The sizes of the faces may vary from specimen to specimen, but the angles between them are always constant. The principal surface layers shown in Figures 2-4 and 2-5 for copper correspond to the faces of a cube (*cubic faces* or *cube faces*); these faces are always at right angles with one another. The smaller surface layer, obtained by cutting off a corner of a cube, is called an *octahedral face*. Native copper, found in deposits of copper ore, often is in the form of crystals with cubic and octahedral faces (Figure 2-2).

Atoms are not hard spheres, but are soft, so that by increased force they may be pushed more closely together (be compressed). This compression occurs, for example, when a copper crystal becomes somewhat smaller in volume under increased pressure. The sizes which are assigned to atoms correspond to the distance between the center of one atom and the center of a neighboring atom of the same kind in a crystal under ordinary circumstances. The distance from a copper atom to each of its twelve nearest neighbors in a copper crystal at room temperature and atmospheric pressure is 2.55 Å; this is called the *diameter* of the copper atom in metallic copper. The radius of the copper atom is half this value.

2–5. *The Molecular Structure of Matter*

Molecular Crystals. The crystal of copper, which we have been discussing as an example of a kind of matter, is built up of *atoms* arranged in a regular pattern. We shall now discuss crystals that contain *discrete groups of atoms* (distinct groups), which are called *molecules*. These crystals are called *molecular crystals*.

An example of a molecular crystal is shown in the upper left part of Figure 2-6, which is a drawing representing the structure of a crystal of the blackish-gray solid substance *iodine*. It is seen that the iodine atoms are grouped together in pairs, to form molecules containing two atoms each. Iodine is used as an example in this section and the following ones because its molecules are simple (containing only two atoms), and because it has been thoroughly studied by scientists.

The distance between the two atoms of iodine in the same molecule

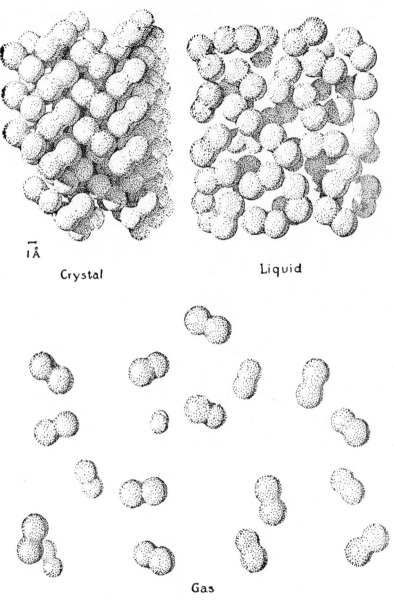

Crystal   Liquid

1 Å

Gas

FIGURE 2-6   *Crystal, liquid, and gaseous iodine, showing diatomic molecules* I_2.

of this molecular crystal is smaller than the distances between atoms in different molecules. The two iodine atoms in each molecule are only 2.70 Å apart, whereas the smallest distance between iodine atoms in different molecules is 3.54 Å.

The forces acting between atoms within a molecule are very strong, and those acting between molecules are weak. As a result of this, it is hard to cause the molecule to change its shape, whereas it is comparatively easy to roll the molecules around relative to one another. For example, under pressure a crystal of iodine decreases in size: the molecules can be pushed together until the distances between iodine atoms in different molecules have decreased by several percent; but the molecules themselves retain their original size, with no appreciable change in interatomic distance within the molecule. When a crystal of iodine at low temperature is heated it expands, so that each of the molecules occupies a larger space in the crystal; but the distance between the two iodine atoms in one molecule stays very close to the normal 2.70 Å.

The molecules of different chemical substances contain varying numbers of atoms, bonded tightly together. An example of a more complicated molecule is shown in Figure 2-7, which represents a portion of a crystal of *naphthalene*. The molecule of naphthalene contains ten carbon atoms, arranged in two hexagonal rings that have one edge in common, and eight hydrogen atoms. Naphthalene is a rather volatile substance, with a characteristic odor. In the form of moth balls, it is used as a moth repellent. The properties of naphthalene are determined by the structure of its molecules.

Photographs of Molecules Made with the Electron Microscope. In the last few years it has finally become possible to see and to photograph molecules. They are too small to be seen with a microscope using ordinary visible light, which cannot permit objects much smaller in diameter than the wavelength of light, about 5000 Å, to be seen. A wonderful new instrument, the *electron microscope*, has now been developed, however, which permits objects a hundred times smaller in diameter to be seen. The electron microscope uses beams of electrons in place of beams of light. Its linear magnifying power is about 100,000, as compared with about 1000 for the ordinary microscope. It

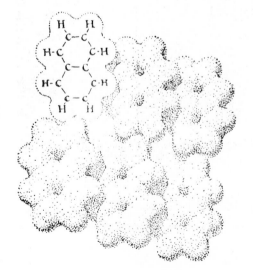

FIGURE 2-7

A portion of a crystal of naphthalene, showing molecules $C_{10}H_8$.

is accordingly possible to see objects as small as 50 Å in diameter with the electron microscope.

Two photographs made with the electron microscope are reproduced here, as Figures 2-8 and 2-9. They show molecules of viruses which cause disease in tomato plants.* Each "bushy stunt" virus molecule is about 230 Å in diameter. It is made of about 750,000 atoms. The "necrosis" virus molecules are somewhat smaller, about 195 Å in diameter. In each photograph the individual molecules can be clearly seen, and in the

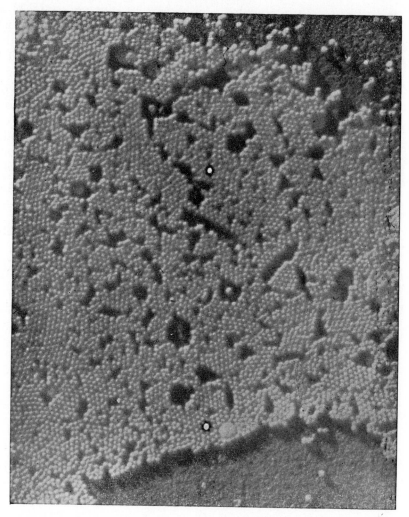

FIGURE 2-8   *Electron micrograph of a single layer of tomato bushy stunt virus molecules. The photograph was made to show added contrast by depositing a very thin layer of gold on the specimen at a small angle, giving the impression of shadows cast by the molecules. Linear magnification 55,000. (From Price, Williams, and Wyckoff, Arch. Biochem., 7, 175, 1946.)*

* A brief discussion of viruses is given in Chapter 31.

photograph of necrosis-virus-protein molecules the regular way in which the molecules arrange themselves in the crystals is evident.

The magnifying power of the electron microscope is not yet great enough to permit ordinary molecules, such as those of naphthalene, to be seen and photographed, but scientists are working on methods of improving the instrument, and perhaps an electron micrograph of naphthalene will be available for inclusion in the third edition of this book.

The Six Crystal Systems.　Chemists often make use of the observed shapes of crystals to help in their identification. The description of the shapes of crystals is the subject of the science of *crystallography*. Every crystal can be classified in one of six crystal systems, called cubic (or isometric), hexagonal, tetragonal, orthorhombic, monoclinic, and triclinic. Characteristic shapes (forms) of crystals of these six systems are shown in Figures 2-10 and 2-11.

2–6. *Evaporation of Crystals. The Nature of a Gas*

At a very low temperature the molecules in a crystal of iodine lie rather quietly in their places in the crystal (Figure 2-6). As the temperature increases the molecules become more and more agitated; each one bounds back and forth more and more vigorously in the little space left for it by its neighbors, and each one strikes its neighbors more and more strongly as it rebounds from them.

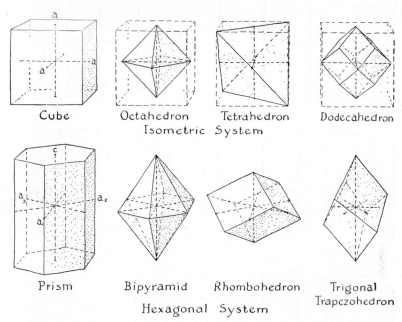

Cube   Octahedron   Tetrahedron   Dodecahedron

Isometric System

Prism   Bipyramid   Rhombohedron   Trigonal Trapezohedron

Hexagonal System

FIGURE 2-10 *Representative crystal forms of the cubic and hexagonal systems.*

A molecule on the surface of the crystal is held to the crystal by the forces of attraction that its neighboring molecules exert on it. Attractive forces of this kind, which are operative between all molecules when they are close together, are called *van der Waals attractive forces* (this name being used because it was the Dutch physicist J. D. van der Waals (1837–1923) who first gave a thorough discussion of intermolecular forces in relation to the nature of gases and liquids).

These attractive forces are quite weak, much weaker than the forces between the atoms in one molecule. Hence occasionally a certain molecule may become so agitated as to break loose from its neighbors, and to fly off into the surrounding space. If the crystal is in a vessel, there will soon be present in the space within the vessel through this process of evaporation a large number of these free molecules, each moving in a straight-line path, and occasionally colliding with another molecule or with the walls of the vessel to change the direction of its motion. These free molecules constitute *iodine vapor* or *iodine gas* (Figure 2-6). The gas molecules are very much like the molecules in the crystal, their interatomic distance being practically the same; it is the distances between molecules that are much larger in a gas than in a crystal.

It may seem surprising that molecules on the surface of a crystal should evaporate directly into a gas, instead of going first through the stage of being in a liquid layer; but in fact the process of slow evaporation of a crystalline substance is not uncommon. Solid pieces of camphor or of naphthalene (as used in moth balls, for example) left out in the

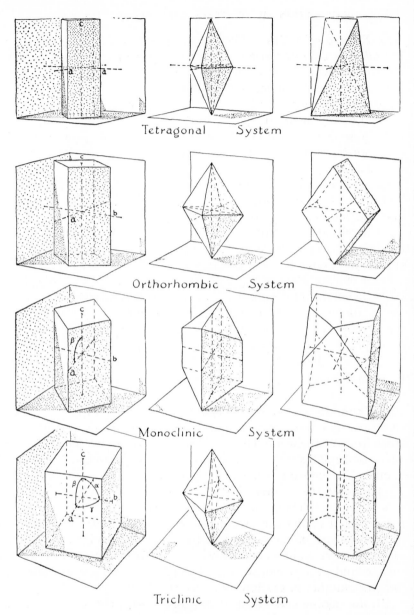

Tetragonal   System

Orthorhombic   System

Monoclinic   System

Triclinic   System

FIGURE 2-11   *Representative crystal forms of the tetragonal, orthorhombic, monoclinic, and triclinic crystal systems.*

air slowly decrease in size, because of the evaporation of molecules from the surface of the solid. Snow may disappear from the ground without melting, by evaporation of the ice crystals at a temperature below that of their melting point. Evaporation is accelerated if a wind is blowing, to take the water vapor away from the immediate neighborhood of the snow crystals, and to prevent the vapor from condensing again on the crystals.

The Nature of a Gas.   The characteristic feature of a gas is that *its molecules are not held together, but are moving about freely, in a volume rather large compared with the volume of the molecules themselves.* The attractive forces between the molecules still operate whenever two molecules come close together, but usually these forces are negligibly small because the molecules are far apart.

Because of the freedom of motion of its molecules a specimen of gas does not have either definite shape or definite size. *A gas shapes itself to its container.*

Gases at ordinary pressure are very dilute—the molecules themselves constitute only about one one-thousandth of the total volume of the gas, the rest being empty space. Thus one gram of solid iodine has a volume of about 0.2 cm³ (its density* is 4.93 g/cm³), whereas one gram of iodine gas at 1 atmosphere pressure and at the temperature 184° C (its boiling point) has a volume of 148 cm³, over 700 times greater. The volume of all of the molecules in a gas is accordingly very small compared with the volume of the gas itself at ordinary pressure. On the other hand, the diameter of a gas molecule is not extremely small compared with the distance between molecules; in a gas at room temperature and 1 atmosphere pressure the average distance from a molecule to its nearest neighbors is about ten times its molecular diameter, as indicated in Figure 2-6†.

The Vapor Pressure of a Crystal.   A crystal of iodine in an evacuated vessel will gradually change into iodine gas by the evaporation of molecules from its surface. Occasionally one of these free gas molecules will again strike the surface of the crystal, and it may stick to the surface, held by the van der Waals attraction of the other crystal molecules. This is called *condensation* of the gas molecules.

The rate at which molecules evaporate from a crystal surface is proportional to the area of the surface, but is essentially independent of the pressure of the surrounding gas, whereas the rate at which gas molecules strike the crystal surface is proportional to the area of the surface and also proportional to the concentration of molecules in the gas (the number of gas molecules in unit volume).

If some iodine crystals are put into a flask, which is then stoppered and allowed to stand at room temperature, it will soon be seen that the gas in the flask has become violet in color, showing that a quantity of iodine has evaporated. After a while it will be evident that the process of evaporation has apparently ceased, because the intensity of colora-

---

* It was mentioned in Section 1–4 that the density of a substance is the mass (weight) of a unit volume of the substance; in the metric system grams per cubic centimeter.

† You will remember that a cube 1 inch on edge has a diameter one tenth as great as that of a cube 10 inches on edge, an area one one-hundredth as great, and a volume one one-thousandth as great.

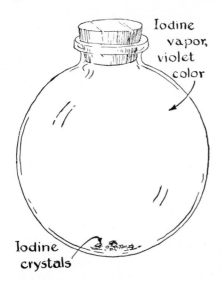

Iodine
vapor,
violet
color

Iodine
crystals

FIGURE 2-12

The evaporation of iodine crystals.

tion of the gas will no longer increase, but will remain constant (Figure 2-12). This steady state is reached when the concentration of gas molecules becomes so great that the rate at which gas molecules strike the crystal surface and stay there is just equal to the rate at which molecules leave the crystal surface. *The corresponding gas pressure is called the* **vapor pressure** *of the crystal.*

A steady state of such a sort is an example of *equilibrium.* It must be

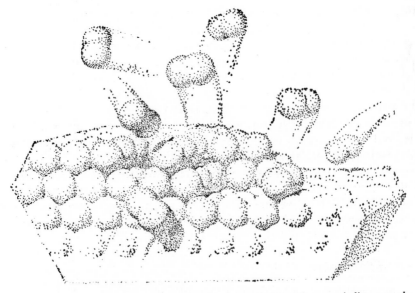

FIGURE 2-13   *Equilibrium between molecules evaporating from an iodine crystal and gas molecules depositing on the crystal.*

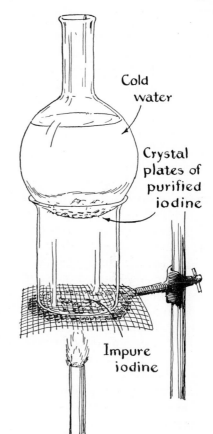

Cold
water

Crystal
plates of
purified
iodine

FIGURE 2-14

The purification of iodine by sublimation.

Impure
iodine

recognized that equilibrium does not represent a situation in which nothing is happening, but rather a situation in which opposing reactions are taking place at the same rate, so as to result in no over-all change. This is indicated in Figure 2-13.

The vapor pressure of iodine increases with increase in temperature. The crystals of iodine which are heated to a temperature only a little below the melting point evaporate rapidly and the vapor may condense into crystals in a cooler part of the vessel. The complete process of evaporation of a crystal and recondensation of a gas directly as crystals, without apparently passing through the liquid state, is called *sublimation*. Sublimation is often a valuable method of purifying a substance; the way in which iodine can be purified by sublimation is shown in Figure 2-14.

2–7. *The Nature of a Liquid*

When iodine crystals are heated to 114° C they melt, forming liquid iodine. The temperature at which the crystals and the liquid are in equilibrium, that is, at which there is no tendency for the crystals to melt or for the liquid to freeze, is called the *melting point* of the crystals, and the *freezing point* of the liquid. This temperature is 114° C for iodine.

Liquid iodine differs from the solid (crystals) mainly in its *fluidity*. It is like the gas in being able to adjust itself to the shape of its container. However, like the solid, and unlike the gas, it has a definite volume, 1 g occupying about 0.2 cm³.

From the molecular viewpoint the process of melting can be described in the following way. As a crystal is heated its molecules become increasingly agitated, and move about more and more vigorously; but this thermal agitation does not carry any one molecule any significant distance away from the position fixed for it by the arrangement of its neighbors in the crystal. At the melting point the agitation finally becomes so great as to cause the molecules to slip by one another and to change somewhat their location relative to one another. They continue to stay close together, but do not continue to retain a regular fixed arrangement; instead the grouping of molecules around a given molecule changes continually, sometimes being much like the close packing of the crystal, in which each iodine molecule has twelve near neighbors, and sometimes considerably different, the molecule having only ten or nine or eight near neighbors, as shown in Figure 2-6. Thus in a liquid, as in a crystal, the molecules are piled rather closely together; but whereas a crystal is characterized by regularity of atomic or molecular arrangement, a liquid is characterized by randomness of structure. The randomness of structure usually causes the density of a liquid to be somewhat less than that of the corresponding crystal; that is, the volume occupied by the liquid is usually somewhat greater than that occupied by the crystal.

The Vapor Pressure and Boiling Point of a Liquid.

A liquid, like a crystal, is, at any temperature, in equilibrium with its own vapor when the vapor molecules are present in a certain concentration. The pressure corresponding to this concentration of gas molecules is called the *vapor pressure of the liquid* at the given temperature.

The vapor pressure of every liquid increases with increasing temperature. *The temperature at which the vapor pressure reaches a standard value (usually 1 atm) is called the* **boiling point** *of the liquid.* At this temperature it is possible for bubbles of the vapor to appear in the liquid and to escape to the surface.

The vapor pressure of liquid iodine reaches 1 atm at 184° C. Hence 184° C is the boiling point of iodine.

Other substances undergo similar changes when they are heated. When copper melts, at 1083° C, it forms liquid copper, in which the arrangement of the copper atoms shows the same sort of randomness as that of the molecules of liquid iodine. Under 1 atm pressure copper

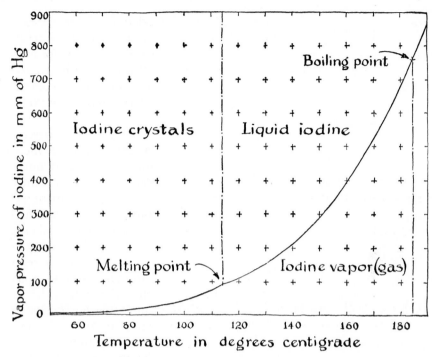

FIGURE 2-15   *A graph showing the vapor-pressure curve of iodine crystal and the vapor-pressure curve of liquid iodine. The melting point of the crystal is the temperature at which the crystal and the liquid have the same vapor pressure, and the boiling point of the liquid (at 1 atm pressure) is the temperature at which the vapor pressure of the liquid equals 1 atm.*

boils at 2310° C to form copper gas; the gas molecules are single copper atoms.

Note that it is customary to refer to the particles that move about in a gas as molecules even though each one may be only a single atom, as in the case of copper.

The Dependence of Vapor Pressure on Temperature.   It has been found by experiment that the vapor pressure of crystals and liquids increases as the temperature is raised. Curves showing the vapor pressure of iodine crystals and liquid iodine are shown in Figure 2-15.

2–8. *The Meaning of Temperature*

In the preceding discussion the assumption has been made that molecules move more rapidly and violently at any given temperature than at a lower one. This assumption is correct—the temperature of a system is a measure of the vigor of motion of all the atoms and molecules in the system.

With increase in temperature there occurs increase in violence of molecular motion of all kinds. Gas molecules rotate more rapidly, and the atoms within a molecule oscil-

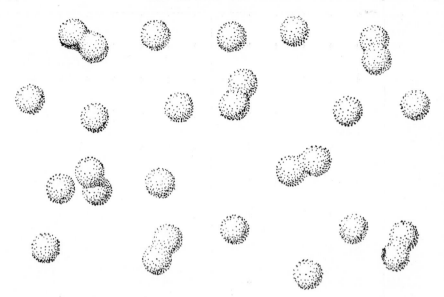

FIGURE 2-16   *Iodine vapor at elevated temperature; this vapor contains both diatomic molecules (I_2) and monatomic molecules (I) of iodine.*

late more rapidly relative to one another. The atoms and molecules in liquids and solids carry out more vigorous vibrational motions. This vigorous motion at high temperatures may result in chemical reaction, especially decomposition of substances. Thus when iodine gas is heated to about 1200° C at 1 atm pressure about one-half of the molecules dissociate (split) into separate iodine atoms (Figure 2-16).

You can get a better understanding of many of the phenomena of chemistry by remembering that the absolute temperature is a measure of the vigor of the motion of atoms and molecules.

Concepts and Terms Introduced in This Chapter

Tested hypotheses become theories or laws. The atomic theory—the most important of all chemical theories.

Atoms—small particles of different kinds, corresponding to the different elements.

Law of conservation of mass. Law of constant proportions. Law of simple multiple proportions.

Modern methods of studying atoms and molecules.

Crystalline copper. Regularity of atomic arrangement in crystals.

Molecule; molecular crystals. Iodine as an example. The six crystal systems.

Evaporation of crystals. Vapor pressure of crystals. Sublimation.

Van der Waals intermolecular forces.

The difference in nature of a crystal, a liquid, and a gas. Vapor pressure, freezing point, and boiling point of a liquid.

The meaning of temperature in relation to molecular motion.

Exercises

2-3. In your own words, define atom, molecule, crystal, liquid, gas.

2-4. Carbon dioxide (Dry Ice) consists of CO_2 molecules. These molecules are linear, with the carbon atom in the center. Make three drawings, representing your concepts of carbon dioxide gas, carbon dioxide liquid, and carbon dioxide crystal.

2-5. Define vapor pressure of a crystal, and also vapor pressure of a liquid. Can you think of an argument showing that these two vapor pressures of a substance must be equal at the melting point?

2-6. The vapor pressure of solid carbon dioxide at its melting point, $-56.5°$ C, is 5 atm. How do you explain the fact that solid carbon dioxide when used for packing ice cream does not melt to form liquid carbon dioxide? If you wanted to make some liquid carbon dioxide, what would you have to do?

2-7. Give an example of a solid material that is crystalline and of one that is not crystalline.

2-8. Classify the following statements as hypotheses, theories, laws, or facts:
   a. The moon is made of limestone.
   b. With a few exceptions, substances increase in volume on melting.
   c. The core of the earth is composed of a metallic form of hydrogen, which has not yet been prepared in the laboratory.
   d. Hydrogen, oxygen, nitrogen, and neon are all gases under ordinary conditions.
   e. All crystals are composed of atoms arranged in a regular way.

2-9. Spectroscopic study of moonlight and sunlight has shown that the reflectivity of the moon (its power of reflecting light of different colors) is not the same as that of limestone. Does this single observed fact eliminate the hypothesis that the moon is composed of limestone? Would you change the name from hypothesis to theory if it had been found that the reflectivity of the moon was (to within experimental error) the same as that of limestone?

2-10. It is stated in the text that copper atoms are 2.55 Å in diameter.
   a. How many Ångströms are there in 1 inch?
   b. How many copper atoms side by side in contact would make a line 1 inch long?
   c. How many atoms of the same size in a simple square array would cover 1 sq. in. of surface?
   d. How many atoms of the same size in a simple cubic array would occupy 1 cu. in.?

2-11. There are about 0.9×10^{24} molecules of water in a cubic inch of water. If a cubic inch of water were poured into the ocean and thoroughly stirred, and a cubic inch of ocean water were then removed, about how many molecules from the original cubic inch would be found in it? Assume the volume of the ocean to correspond to an average depth of 1 mile over the entire surface of the earth.

2-12. If the molecules in a glass of water (say 10 cu. in.) were to be increased in diameter a millionfold, making each molecule the size of a small grain of sand, to what depth could the surface of the earth be covered uniformly with the enlarged molecules?

2-13. Arrange marbles, steel balls, or other spheres of the same size in a close-packed layer, such that each sphere is surrounded by six spheres in contact with it. Pack a similar layer on top of the first one, so that each sphere in the second layer is in the pocket formed by the three spheres in the lower layer. Note that a third layer could then be put directly above the first layer, or in another position; the second of these alternatives, repeated, leads to the structure of the copper crystal. Repeat this process to build a triangular pyramid. Note that this pyramid is a regular tetrahedron.

2-14. Describe qualitatively the structure of a crystal of iodine, of liquid iodine, of gaseous iodine at low temperature, and of gaseous iodine at high temperature.

2-15. What is the effect of increase in pressure on the boiling point of a liquid? Estimate the boiling point of liquid iodine at a pressure of $\frac{1}{2}$ atm (see Figure 2-15).

2-16. Camphor sublimes at 205° C. What is this temperature in °F? Can you suggest a way of extracting camphor from the leaves and wood of the camphor tree?

Reference Books

A somewhat more detailed discussion of the atomic structure of crystals than that given above can be found in Chapter 2 of L. Pauling, *General Chemistry*, 2nd Ed., W. H. Freeman and Company, San Francisco, **1953.**

A simple discussion of x-rays and the x-ray diffraction method of determining the structure of crystals is given in Chapter 3 of *General Chemistry*. For more detailed discussions see W. H. Bragg and W. L. Bragg, *X-Rays and Crystal Structure*, Harcourt, Brace and Co., New York, **1924,** or the article X-Rays and Crystal Structure in the Encyclopaedia Britannica, 14th Ed.

A simple account of the determination of the structure of gas molecules by the diffraction of electrons has been given by R. Spurr and L. Pauling, *Journal of Chemical Education,* **18,** 458 (1941**).**

Chapter 3

The Electron and
the Nuclei of Atoms

In the preceding chapter we have discussed the atomic theory, and have seen that some of the properties of substances can be explained by this theory. The two substances copper and iodine, which were used as the principal examples in the discussion, have different properties because their atoms are different.

Chemists of the nineteenth century asked whether it might be possible to understand the differences between atoms of different elements, such as copper and iodine, but they were not able to answer the question. About fifty years ago, however, it was discovered that atoms themselves are composed of still smaller particles. The discovery of the components of atoms and the investigation of the structure of atoms—the ways in which atoms of different kinds are built of the smaller particles—constitute one of the most interesting stories in the history of science. Moreover, knowledge about the structure of atoms has during recent years permitted the facts of chemistry to be systematized in a striking way, making the subject easier to understand and to remember. The student of chemistry can be helped greatly in mastering his subject by first obtaining a good understanding of atomic structure.

The particles that constitute atoms are *electrons* and *atomic nuclei*. Electrons and atomic nuclei carry electric charges, and these electric charges are in large part responsible for the properties of the particles and for the structure of atoms. We shall accordingly begin this chapter with a discussion of the nature of electricity.

3–1. *The Nature of Electricity*

The ancient Greeks knew that when a piece of amber is rubbed with wool or fur it achieves the power of attracting light objects, such as feathers or bits of straw. This phenomenon was studied by William Gilbert (1540–1603), Queen Elizabeth I's physician, who invented the adjective *electric* to describe the force of attraction, after the Greek word *elektron*, meaning amber. Gilbert and many other scientists, including Benjamin Franklin, investigated electric phenomena, and during the nineteenth century many discoveries about the nature of electricity, and of magnetism (which is closely related to electricity), were made.

It was found that if a rod of sealing wax, which behaves in the same way as amber, is rubbed with a woolen cloth, and a rod of glass is rubbed with a silken cloth, an electric spark will pass between the sealing-wax rod and the glass rod when they are brought near one another. Moreover, it was found that a force of attraction operates between them. If the sealing-wax rod that has been electrically charged by rubbing with a woolen cloth is suspended from a thread, as shown in Figure 3-1, and the charged glass rod is brought near one end of it, this end will turn toward the glass rod. An electrified sealing-wax rod is repelled, however, by a similar sealing-wax rod, and also an electrified glass rod is repelled by a similar glass rod (Figure 3-1).

Through the experimental study of such phenomena, the ideas were developed that there are two kinds of electricity, which were called resinous electricity (that which is picked up by the sealing-wax rod) and vitreous electricity (that which is picked up by the glass rod), and that the two kinds of electricity attract one another, whereas each kind repels itself. Franklin simplified this picture of electricity somewhat, by assuming that only one kind of electricity can flow from an object to another object. He assumed that when a glass rod is rubbed with a silken cloth this electric "fluid" is transferred from the cloth to the glass rod, and he described the glass rod as *positively charged*, meaning that it had an excess of the electric fluid. He described the cloth as having a deficiency of the electric fluid, and being *negatively charged*. He pointed out that he did not really know whether the electric fluid had been

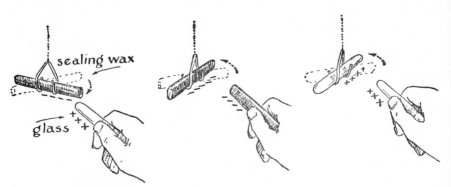

FIGURE 3-1   *Experiments showing the attraction of unlike charges of electricity and the repulsion of like charges.*

transferred from the silken cloth to the glass rod or from the glass rod to the silken cloth, and that accordingly the decision to describe vitreous electricity as positive (involving an excess of electric fluid) was an arbitrary one. We now know, in fact, that when the glass rod is rubbed with a silken cloth negatively charged particles, the electrons, are transferred from the glass rod to the silken cloth, and that Franklin thus made the wrong decision in his assumption.

Units of Electric Charge.   The unit of electric charge in the metric system is called the *statcoulomb*. (The definition of this unit is given in textbooks of physics.) In practical work there is need for a larger unit of electric charge. The larger unit that has been adopted is the *coulomb*, which is closely equal to 3×10^9 statcoulombs:

1 coulomb $= 3 \times 10^9$ statcoulombs

3–2. *The Discovery of the Electron*

The idea that there are electric particles in substances was proposed, as a hypothesis, by G. Johnstone Stoney, an English scientist. Stoney knew that substances can be decomposed by an electric current—for example, water can be decomposed into hydrogen and oxygen in this way. He also knew that Michael Faraday had found that a definite amount of electricity is needed to liberate a certain amount of an element from one of its compounds. The experiment carried out by Faraday will be discussed in Chapter 10 of our book. In 1874, after thinking about these facts, Stoney stated that they indicate that *electricity exists in discrete units*, and that these units are associated with atoms. In 1891 he suggested the name *electron* for his postulated unit of electricity. The discovery of the electron by experiment was made in 1897 by Sir J. J. Thomson (1856–1940), in Cambridge University, England.*

The Properties of the Electron.   The electron is a particle with a negative electric charge of magnitude -4.802×10^{-10} statcoulombs, or -1.601×10^{-19} coulombs.

The mass of the electron is 9.107×10^{-28} g, which is 1/1837 of the mass of the hydrogen atom.

The electron is very small. The radius of the electron cannot be determined exactly, but it is known to be about 1×10^{-12} cm. Since atoms have radii of about 1×10^{-8} cm, the electron is only about 1/10,000 as large as an atom.

* The experiments that led to the discovery of the electron are described in Section 3-7.

3–3. *The Flow of Electricity in a Metal*

Knowledge of the existence of electrons permits us to discuss some of the properties of electricity in a simple way.

In a metal or similar conductor of electricity there are electrons which have considerable freedom of motion, and which move along between the atoms of the metal when an electric potential difference is applied. A direct current of electricity passing along a copper wire is a *flow of electrons* along the wire.

Let us call to mind the analogy between the flow of electricity along a wire and the flow of water in a pipe. *Quantity* of water is measured in liters or cubic feet; quantity of electricity is usually measured either in *coulombs* or in *statcoulombs*. *Rate of flow*, or *current*, of water, the quantity passing a given point of the pipe in unit time, is measured in liters per second, or cubic feet per second; current of electricity is measured in *amperes* (coulombs per second). The rate of flow of water in a pipe depends on the *difference in the pressures* at the two ends of the pipe, with atmospheres or pounds per square inch as units. The current of electricity in a wire depends on the *electric potential difference* or *voltage drop* between its ends, which is usually measured in *volts*. The definitions of the unit of quantity of electricity (the coulomb) and the unit of electric potential (the volt) have been made by international agreement.

An electric generator is essentially an electron pump, which pumps electrons out of one wire and into another. A generator of direct current pumps electrons continually in the same direction, and one of alternating current reverses its pumping direction regularly, thus building up electron pressure first in one direction and then in the other. A 60-cycle generator reverses its pumping direction 120 times per second.

Illustrative Exercises

3-1.   An ordinary electric light bulb is operated under conditions such that one ampere of current (one coulomb per second) is passing through the filament. How many electrons pass through the filament each second? (Remember that the charge of the electron is -1.60×10^{-19} coulombs.)

3-2.   If a golf ball could be magnified 250,000,000 times, making it as big as the earth, each atom (3 or 4 Å in diameter) would become 3 or 4 inches in diameter. Would the electrons then look like peas, or birdshot, or fine grains of sand, or particles of dust?

3–4. *The Nuclei of Atoms*

In 1911 the British physicist Ernest Rutherford carried out some experiments[*] which showed that every atom contains, in addition to one or more electrons, another particle, called the *nucleus* of the atom. Every nucleus has a positive electric charge. It is very small, being only about as big as an electron (about 10^{-12} cm in diameter), and it is very heavy—the lightest nucleus is 1836 times as heavy as an electron.

There are many different kinds of nuclei; those of the atoms of one element are different from those of every other element. The nucleus of the hydrogen atom has the same electric charge as the electron, but

---

[*] These experiments are described in later sections of this chapter.

with opposite sign, positive instead of negative. The nuclei of other atoms have positive charges that are multiples of this fundamental charge.

3–5. *The Proton and the Neutron*

The *proton* is the simplest atomic nucleus. It is the nucleus of the most abundant kind of hydrogen atom, which is the lightest of all atoms.

The proton has an electric charge 4.802×10^{-10} statcoulomb or 1.601×10^{-19} coulomb. This charge is exactly the same as that of the electron, except that it is positive, whereas the charge of the electron is negative.

The mass of the proton is 1.672×10^{-24} g. This is 1836 times the mass of the electron.

The *neutron* was discovered by the English physicist James Chadwick in 1932. The mass of the neutron is 1.675×10^{-24} g, which is 1839 times the mass of the electron. The neutron has no electric charge.

It is customary for chemists to use an *atomic mass unit*, which is approximately the mass of the proton. Both the proton and the neutron have masses which are approximately one atomic mass unit.

3–6. *The Structure of Atomic Nuclei*

Several hundred different kinds of atomic nuclei are known to exist. Together with the electrons that surround them, they make up the atoms of the different chemical elements. At the present time physicists all over the world are working on the problem of the structure of atomic nuclei. They have not yet solved this problem, although they have learned a great deal about the properties of the nuclei, and the ways in which they can be made from other particles or converted into other particles. This phase of chemistry, which we call *nuclear chemistry*, is discussed in Chapter 32 of our book.

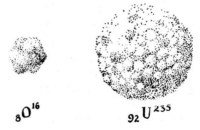

$_1\text{H}^1$ $_1\text{H}^2$ $_2\text{He}^4$
Proton Deuteron Alpha particle

FIGURE 3-2

Hypothetical structures of some atomic nuclei. We do not yet know just how these nuclei are constructed out of elementary particles, but it is known that nuclei are approximately 10^{-12} cm in diameter, and are, accordingly, very small even compared with atoms.

$_8\text{O}^{16}$ $_{92}\text{U}^{235}$

Although the detailed structures of nuclei are not known, physicists seem to be agreed in accepting the idea that they can all be described as being built up of protons and neutrons.

Let us first discuss, as an example, the *deuteron*. This is the nucleus of the *heavy hydrogen atom*, or *deuterium atom*. The deuteron has the same electric charge as the proton, but has about twice the mass of the proton. It is thought that the deuteron is made of one proton and one neutron, as indicated in Figure 3-2.

The nucleus of the helium atom, which is also called the *alpha particle*, has electric charge twice as great as that of the proton, and mass about four times as great as that of the proton. It is thought that the alpha particle is composed of two protons and two neutrons.

In Figure 3-2 there is also shown a drawing representing the nucleus of an oxygen atom, composed of eight protons and eight neutrons. The electric charge of this nucleus is eight times the electric charge of the proton. This electric charge would accordingly be neutralized by the negative charges of eight electrons. The mass of this oxygen nucleus is about 16 mass units.

There is also shown in the figure a hypothetical drawing of the nucleus of a uranium atom. This nucleus is composed of 92 protons and 143 neutrons. The electric charge of this nucleus is 92 times that of the proton; it would be neutralized by the negative charges of 92 electrons. The mass of this nucleus is about 235 times the mass of the proton.

In thinking about atoms and atomic nuclei, you must remember that the drawings of atomic nuclei in Figure 3-2 correspond to a magnification ten thousand times greater than the drawings of atoms and molecules that are shown elsewhere in this book. The nuclei are very small, even compared with atoms.

We shall continue the discussion of atomic nuclei of different kinds, and atoms of different kinds, in the following chapter.

3–7. *The Experiments That Led to the Discovery of the Electron*

Many interesting experiments involving electricity were carried out by physicists during the nineteenth century. These experiments ultimately led to the discovery of the electron. In order to understand them it is necessary to know something about the way in which the motion of an electrically charged particle is affected by other electric charges or by a magnet.

The Interaction of an Electric Charge with Other Electric Charges and with Magnets. An electric charge is said to be surrounded by an *electric field*, which exercises a force, either of attraction or of repulsion, on any other electric charge in its neighborhood. The strength of an electric field can be measured by determining the force that operates on a unit of electric charge.

In experimental work use is often made of an apparatus like that shown in Figure

FIGURE 3-3

The motion of an electrically charged particle in the uniform electric field between charged plates.

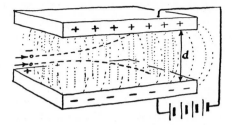

3-3, in which two large parallel plates of metal are held a small, constant distance from one another. By use of a battery or generator of electricity, one of these parallel plates is charged positively (that is, some electrons are taken away from it), and the other is charged negatively.

A wire or plate which has an excess of positive charge is called an *anode*. A wire or plate which has an excess of negative electric charge is called a *cathode*. In Figure 3-3 the upper plate is the anode and the lower plate is the cathode.

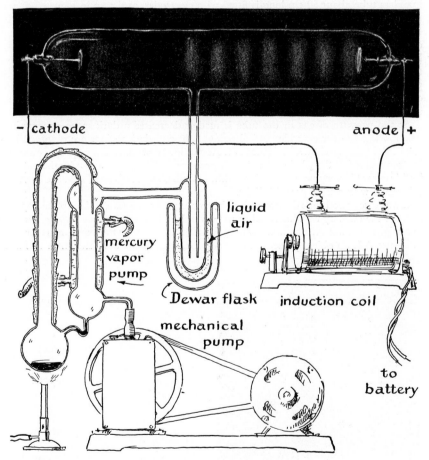

FIGURE 3-4   *Apparatus used to observe the discharge of electricity in a gas at low pressure. The dark space around the cathode is called the Crookes dark space; at still lower pressures the Crookes dark space fills the whole tube.*

A particle with negative electric charge placed between the plates would be attracted toward the upper plate and repelled from the lower plate. It would accordingly move in the direction of the upper plate. Similarly, a particle with positive electric charge placed between the plates would move toward the lower plate.

The force exerted on a positive charge by the electric field between the plates has the same effect as the force exerted on a mass by the gravitational field of the earth. Accordingly a positively charged particle shot into the region between the plates, as indicated in Figure 3-3, would fall to the bottom plate along the path indicated by the dashed line, in the same way that a rock thrown horizontally would fall toward the surface of the earth.

You know that a piece of iron or steel can be magnetized, to form a *magnet*, and that the magnet has the power of attracting other pieces of iron. A magnet also has the power of exerting a force on any electrically charged particle that shoots by it. A magnet can hence also be used to study charged particles.

The Discovery of the Electron. During the nineteenth century many physicists carried out experiments on the conduction of electricity through gases. For example, if a glass tube about 50 cm long is fitted with electrodes, as shown in Figure 3-4, and a potential of about 10,000 volts is applied between the electrodes, no electricity is at first conducted between the electrodes. If, however, some of the air in the tube is pumped out, by use of pumps such as those indicated in the lower part of the figure, electricity begins to be conducted through the tube. While the electricity is being conducted through the tube light is emitted by the gas in the tube. You are familiar with this phenomenon, because you have seen many neon lamps in street signs. These neon lamps contain the gas neon, or some other gas, which is caused to emit light when electricity is conducted through the gas.

As the pressure of gas in the tube is further decreased a dark space appears in the neighborhood of the cathode, and alternate light and dark regions are observed in the rest of the tube, as shown in Figure 3-4. At still lower pressure the dark space increases in size until it fills the whole tube. At this pressure no light is given out by the gas which is still present in very small quantity within the tube, but the glass of the tube itself glows (*fluoresces*) with a faint greenish light.

It was discovered that the greenish light coming from the glass is due to the bombardment of the glass by rays liberated at the cathode. These rays, called *cathode rays*, travel in straight lines from the cathode to the glass. This is shown by the experiment illustrated in Figure 3-5: an object placed within the tube, such as the cross shown in this figure,

FIGURE 3-5

Experiment showing that cathode rays, starting from the cathode at the left, move through the Crookes tube in straight lines.

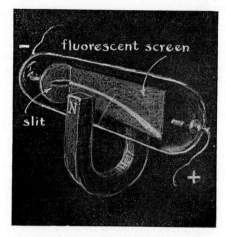

FIGURE 3-6

Experiment showing that the cathode rays have a negative charge.

casts a shadow on the glass—the glass fluoresces everywhere except in the region of this shadow.

It was shown by the French scientist Jean Perrin (1870–1942) in 1895 that these cathode rays consist of particles with a negative electric charge, rather than a positive charge. His experiment is illustrated in Figure 3-6. He introduced a shield with a slit in the tube, so as to form a beam of cathode rays. He also placed a fluorescent screen* in the tube, so that the path of the beam could be followed by the trace of the fluorescence. When a magnet was placed near the tube the beam was observed to be deflected in the direction corresponding to the presence of a negative charge on the particles.

J. J. Thomson then carried out some experiments that permitted him to make some quantitative statements about the particles that constitute the cathode rays. He used the apparatus shown in Figure 3-7, in which a beam of cathode rays can be affected by

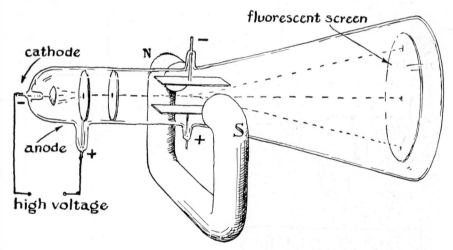

FIGURE 3-7   *The apparatus used by J. J. Thomson to determine the ratio of electric charge to mass of the cathode rays, through the simultaneous deflection of the rays by an electric field and a magnetic field.*

* A fluorescent screen is a sheet of paper or glass coated with a substance that shines when it is struck by electrons.

either a magnet that is brought up beside the tube, or by an electric field, produced by applying an electric potential to the two metal plates in the tube, or by both the magnet and the electric field. The effect on the beam of cathode rays was observed by use of a fluorescent screen. The results of his experiment convinced Thomson that the cathode-ray particles constitute a form of matter different from ordinary forms of matter. The particles were indicated by Thomson's experiments to be much lighter than atoms. Later and more accurate experiments showed that the mass of the cathode-ray particle is only 1/1837 times the mass of the hydrogen atom.

Although other investigators had carried out important experiments on cathode rays, the quantitative experiments by Thomson provided the first convincing evidence that these rays consist of particles (electrons) much lighter than atoms, and Thomson is hence given the credit for discovering the electron.

The Determination of the Charge of the Electron. After the discovery of the electron by Thomson, many investigators worked on the problem of determining accurately the charge of the electron. The American physicist R. A. Millikan (1868–1953), who began his experiments in 1906, was the most successful of the earlier experimenters. By means of his oil-drop experiment he determined the value of the charge of the electron to within one percent in 1909.

The apparatus that he used is illustrated in Figure 3-8. Small drops of oil are formed by a sprayer, and some of them attach themselves to electrons that have been separated from molecules by action of a beam of x-rays. The experimenter watches one of these small oil drops through a microscope. He first measures the rate at which it falls in the earth's gravitational field. The small drops fall at a rate determined by their size, and measurement of the rate of fall of a drop permits the investigator to calculate the size.

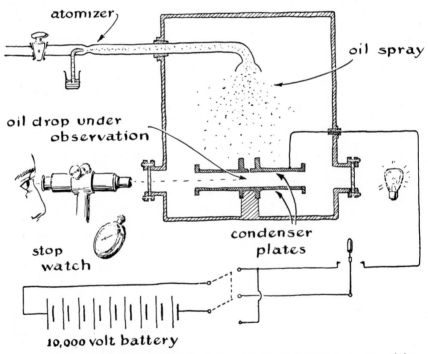

FIGURE 3-8 *A diagram of the apparatus used by R. A. Millikan in determining the charge of the electron by the oil-drop method.*

When the electric field is turned on, by charging the plates above and below the region where the oil drops are moving, some of the drops, which carry no electric charge, continue to fall as before. Other drops, carrying electric charges, change their speed, and may rise, being pulled up by the attraction of the electric charge for the oppositely charged upper plate in the apparatus. The rate of a drop that has been watched falling is then observed. From these measurements, the magnitude of the electric charge on the drop can be calculated. In various experiments with different oil drops, values such as the following were obtained for the electric charge on the drop:

Charge $= 4.8 \times 10^{-10}$ statcoulombs

Charge $= 9.6 \times 10^{-10} = 2 \times 4.8 \times 10^{-10}$

Charge $= 4.8 \times 10^{-10}$

Charge $= 24.0 \times 10^{-10} = 5 \times 4.8 \times 10^{-10}$

All of these values have a common factor, 4.8×10^{-10} statcoulombs. Millikan accordingly concluded that this is the smallest electric charge that can occur under these conditions, and he identified it with the charge of the electron.

Since Millikan carried out his work, a number of other methods have been developed for determining the charge of the electron, and its value is now known to about 0.01 percent.

3–8. *The Discovery of X-Rays and Radioactivity*

Several great scientific discoveries were made in a period of a few years, beginning in 1895. These discoveries made great changes in chemistry as well as in physics. X-rays were discovered in 1895, radioactivity was discovered in 1896, the new radioactive elements polonium and radium were isolated in the same year, and the electron was discovered in 1897.

Wilhelm Konrad Röntgen (1845–1923), Professor of Physics in the University of Würzburg, Germany, reported in 1895 that he had discovered a new kind of rays, which he called x-rays. These rays are produced when electricity is passed through a tube such as that shown in Figure 3-4. The rays are outside of the tube; they radiate from the place where the cathode-ray electrons strike the glass. They have the power of passing through matter that is opaque to ordinary light, and of exposing a photographic plate. Within a few weeks after the announcement of this great discovery x-rays were being used by physicians for the investigation of patients with broken bones and other disorders.

Soon after the discovery of x-rays the French physicist Henri Becquerel (1852–1908) investigated some minerals containing uranium. He found that these minerals emit

FIGURE 3-9

A simple electroscope. When an electric charge is present on the gold foil and its support, the two leaves of the foil separate, because of the repulsion of like electric charges.

rays that, like x-rays, can pass through black paper and other opaque materials and expose a photographic plate. He also found that the radiation produced by the uranium minerals could, like x-rays, discharge an electroscope (Figure 3-9), by making the air conductive.

Marie Sklodowska Curie (1867–1934) then began a systematic investigation of "Bequerel radiation," using the electroscope as a test. She investigated many substances, to see if they were similar to uranium in producing rays. She found that natural pitchblend, an ore of uranium, is several times more active than purified uranium oxide.

With her husband, Professor Pierre Curie (1859–1906), she began to separate pitchblend into fractions and to determine their activity in discharging the electroscope. She isolated a fraction that was 400 times more active than uranium. This fraction consisted largely of bismuth sulfide. Since pure bismuth sulfide is not radioactive, she assumed that a new, strongly radioactive element, similar in chemical properties to bismuth, was present as a contaminant. This element, which she named *polonium*, was the first element discovered through its properties of radioactivity. In the same year, 1896, the Curies isolated another new radioactive element, which they named *radium*.

In 1899 Ernest Rutherford, working in the Cavendish Laboratory in Cambridge, England, under J. J. Thomson, reported that the radiation from uranium is of at least two distinct types, which he called alpha radiation and beta radiation. A French investigator, P. Villard, soon reported that a third kind of radiation, gamma radiation, is also emitted.

Alpha, Beta, and Gamma Rays.   The experiments showing the presence of three kinds of rays emitted by natural radioactive materials are illustrated by Figure 3-10. The rays, formed into a beam by passing along a narrow hole in a lead block, traverse a strong magnetic field. They are affected in three different ways, showing that the three kinds of rays have different electric charges. Alpha rays carry a positive electric charge. Beta rays carry a negative electric charge, and are deflected by a magnet in the opposite direction to the alpha rays. Gamma rays do not carry an electric charge, and are not deflected by the magnet.

Rutherford found that the alpha rays, after they are slowed down, produce the gas helium. Further studies made by him showed definitely that the *alpha rays are the positively charged parts of helium atoms*, moving at high speeds. The *beta rays are electrons*, also moving at high speeds—they are similar in nature to the cathode rays produced in an electric discharge tube. *Gamma rays are a form of radiant energy, similar to visible light.* They are identical with x-rays produced in an x-ray tube operated at very high voltage.

The identification of the positively charged alpha particles with helium atoms was made by Rutherford by an experiment in which he allowed alpha particles to be shot through a thin metal foil into a chamber, and later was able to show that helium

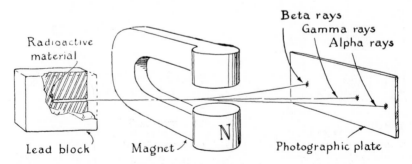

FIGURE 3-10   *The deflection of alpha rays and beta rays by a magnetic field.*

is present in the chamber. He could, moreover, correlate the amount of helium in the chamber with the number of alpha particles that had passed through the foil.

3–9. *The Discovery of the Nuclei of Atoms*

In 1911 Rutherford carried out the experiment that showed that most of the mass of atoms is concentrated in particles that are very small in size compared with the atoms themselves.

His experiment consisted in bombarding a film of some substance, a piece of metal foil, with a stream of fast-moving alpha particles, and observing the direction in which the alpha particles rebound from the atoms. The nature of the experiment is indicated by the drawing in Figure 3-11. A piece of radium emits alpha particles in all directions. A narrow hole in a lead block defines a beam of the alpha particles. This beam of alpha particles then passes through the metal foil, and the directions in which the alpha particles continue to move are observed. The direction in which an alpha particle moves can be detected by use of a screen coated with zinc sulfide. When an alpha particle strikes the screen a flash of light is sent out.

If the atoms bombarded with alpha particles were solid throughout their volume, we should expect all of the alpha particles in the beam to be deflected to some extent. Actually, however, Rutherford observed that most of the alpha particles passed through the metal foil without appreciable deflection: in one experiment, in which the alpha particles were sent through a gold foil 4000 Å thick, so that they penetrated about 1000 layers of atoms, only about one alpha particle in 100,000 was deflected. This one usually showed a great deflection, often through more than 90°, as indicated in the figure. When foil twice as thick was taken, it was found that about twice as many alpha particles showed deflection through large angles, with most of them still passing straight through.

These experimental results can be understood if the assumption is made that *most of the mass of the atom is concentrated into a very small particle*, which Rutherford called the atomic nucleus. If the alpha particle were also very small, then the chance of collision of these two very small particles as the alpha particle passed through the atom would be

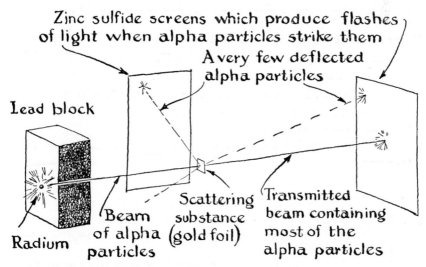

FIGURE 3-11 *A diagram representing the experiment carried out by Rutherford, which showed that atoms contain very small, heavy atomic nuclei.*

small. Most of the alpha particles could pass through the foil without striking any atomic nucleus, and these alpha particles would not then be deflected.

Since about one particle in 100,000 is deflected on passing through a foil consisting of 1000 atom layers, only about one particle in 100,000,000 would be deflected by a single layer of atoms. Rutherford concluded from this that the heavy nucleus has a cross-sectional area only 0.00000001 as great as the cross-sectional area of the atom, and hence that the diameter of the nucleus is only 1/10,000 as great as the diameter of the atom (the square root of 0.00000001 is 1/10,000).

Since atoms are a few Ångströms in diameter, the diameter of the nucleus is indicated to be approximately 10^{-4} Å or 10^{-12} cm. The atomic nucleus is hence about as big as an electron, which is about 10^{-12} cm in diameter.

The picture of the atom that has been developed from this experiment and similar experiments is indeed an extraordinary one. If we could magnify a piece of gold leaf by the linear factor 1,000,000,000—a billion fold—we would see it as an immense pile of atoms about two feet in diameter, each atom thus being about as big as a bushel basket. Practically the entire mass of each atom would, however, be concentrated in a single particle, the nucleus, about 0.001 inch in diameter, like an extremely small grain of sand. This nucleus would be surrounded by electrons, equally small, and moving very rapidly about. Rutherford's experiment would correspond to shooting through a pile of these bushel-basket atoms a stream of minute grains of sand, each of which would continue in a straight line unless it happened to collide with one of the minute grains of sand representing the nuclei of the atoms. It is obvious that the chance of such a collision would be very small. (The alpha particles are not deflected by the electrons in the atoms, because they are very much heavier than the electrons.)

Because of the new knowledge of the nature of atoms that it led to, Rutherford's experiment must be considered one of the most important experiments that any man has ever made.

Concepts and Terms Introduced in This Chapter

The nature of electricity. Repulsion of two electric charges with the same sign (both positive or both negative). Attraction of opposite electric charges (one positive and one negative).

Units of electric charge: statcoulomb, coulomb.

The electron. Its charge (negative) and mass (small).

The flow of electricity in a metal—a flow of electrons.

The nuclei of atoms. Proton, neutron. Heavier nuclei contain protons and neutrons.

The experiments that led to the discovery of the electron. Millikan's oil-drop experiment, giving the value of the charge of the electron.

Discovery of x-rays and radioactivity. Alpha, beta, and gamma rays. Rutherford's experiment.

Exercises

3-3. The helium nucleus is made of two protons and two neutrons. How many electrons must attach themselves to this nucleus to make a helium atom, which has no electric charge?

3-4 The uranium nucleus contains 92 protons. How many electrons are there in a uranium atom?

3-5. Describe the motion of a charged particle moving between two parallel metal plates, one of which is positively charged and one negatively charged.

3-6. Describe Perrin's experiment, which led him to conclude that cathode-ray particles (electrons) have a negative electric charge.

3-7. Describe the Rutherford experiment that led him to discover that atoms contain a very small, heavy nucleus.

3-8. What are alpha particles? Beta particles? Gamma rays?

Reference Books

R. F. Humphreys and R. Beringer, *First Principles of Atomic Physics*, Harper & Brothers, New York, **1950**.

H. E. White, *Classical and Modern Physics*, D. Van Nostrand Co., New York, **1950**.

S. Glasstone, *Sourcebook on Atomic Energy*, D. Van Nostrand Co., New York, **1950**.

Chapter 4

Elements,
Elementary Substances,
and Compounds

One of the most important parts of chemical theory is the division of substances into the two classes *elementary substances* and *compounds*. This division was achieved about a century and a half ago, principally through the efforts of the French chemist Lavoisier.

The arguments which Lavoisier and other early chemists used to decide whether a substance is an elementary substance or a compound have been briefly discussed in Chapter 1. During recent years more straightforward and definite methods have been found for identifying elementary substances. These methods, developed by physicists, involve the determination of the electric charge of the atomic nuclei (the number of unit electric charges). The power of the new methods has caused the definitions of the words element, elementary substance, and compound to be changed in recent years.

4–1. *The Chemical Elements*

A kind of matter consisting of atoms which all have nuclei with the same electric charge is called an **element.**

For example, all of the atoms which contain nuclei with the charge $+e$, each nucleus having one electron attached to it to neutralize its charge, comprise the element hydrogen, and all of the atoms which contain nuclei with the charge $+92e$ comprise the element uranium.

All pure substances can be divided into two classes: elementary substances, and compounds.

An **elementary substance** *is a substance that is composed of atoms of one element only.*

A **compound** *is a substance that is composed of atoms of two or more different elements.* These atoms of two or more different elements must be present in a definite numerical ration, since substances are defined as having a definite composition (Sections 1–3, 2–2).

Hydrogen, carbon, nitrogen, oxygen, sodium, iron, copper, zinc, lead, tin, silver, gold, chlorine, iodine, sulfur, and phosphorus are common elements; one hundred different elements in all are known at the present time.

Common salt, sugar, and baking soda are well-known compounds. Common salt contains atoms of two elements—atoms of sodium and atoms of chlorine. Sugar contains atoms of carbon, hydrogen, and oxygen, and baking soda contains atoms of sodium, hydrogen, carbon, and oxygen. Several hundred thousand different chemical compounds are now known, and many new ones are made every year.

Atomic Number. The electric charge of the nucleus of an atom, in units equal to the charge on the proton, is called the *atomic number* of the atom. It is usually given the symbol Z, the electric charge of a nucleus with atomic number Z being Z times e, with the charge of the proton equal to e, and the charge of the electron equal to $-e$. Thus the simplest atom, that of hydrogen, has atomic number 1; it consists of a nucleus with electric charge e, and an electron with electric charge $-e$. Uranium has atomic number 92.

The one hundred elements that have so far been discovered or made by scientists represent all the atomic numbers from 1 to 101.

The Assignment of Atomic Numbers to the Elements. Soon after the discovery of the electron as a constituent of matter it was recognized that elements might be assigned atomic numbers, representing the number of electrons in an atom of each element, but the way of doing this correctly was not known until 1913. In that year, H. G. J. Moseley (1887–1915), a young English physicist working in the University of Manchester, found that the atomic number of any element could be determined by the study of the x-rays emitted by an x-ray tube containing the element. By a few months of experimental work he was able to assign their correct atomic numbers to many elements.

A brief account of Moseley's experiment is given in Section 4–8, at the end of this Chapter.

Isotopes. It was mentioned in Chapter 3 that sometimes different atomic nuclei (with different mass) have the same electric charge. For example, the proton has electric charge $+e$, and the deuteron, which is built of a proton and a neutron, also has electric charge $+e$. The two nuclei differ in their mass, the deuteron having about twice the mass of the proton. When the proton combines with an electron a hydrogen atom is formed. Similarly, when a deuteron combines with an electron a hydrogen atom is formed, which differs from the light hydrogen atom in having a heavier nucleus. A third kind of hydrogen atom is also known. Its nucleus, called the *triton*, consists of a proton and two neutrons. Each of these three nuclei contains one proton, and hence has electric charge $+e$, and atomic number 1.

The *protium* atom, containing a proton as its nucleus, the *deuterium* atom, containing a deuteron as its nucleus, and the *tritium* atom, containing a triton as its nucleus, are three different kinds of hydrogen atoms, all equal in atomic number ($Z = 1$) and electric charge ($+e$) of their nuclei, but differing in mass. These three kinds of atoms are called the *isotopes* of hydrogen.*

The **isotopes** *of an element are atoms whose nuclei contain the same number of protons (equal to the atomic number of the element) but different numbers of neutrons.*

All known elements have two or more isotopes. In some cases (such as aluminum) only one isotope occurs naturally, the others being unstable. The maximum number of stable isotopes of any element is 10, possessed by tin.

The chemical properties of all the isotopes of an element are essentially the same. These properties are determined in the main by the atomic number of the nucleus, and not by its mass.

The Names and Symbols of the Elements.

The names of the elements are given in order of atomic number in Table 4-1. The chemical symbols of the elements, used as abbreviations for their names, are also given in the table. These symbols are usually the initial letters of the names, plus another letter when necessary. In some cases the initial letters of Latin names are used: Fe for iron (ferrum), Cu for copper (cuprum), Ag for silver (argentum), Au for gold (aurum), Hg for mercury (hydrargyrum). The system of chemical symbols was proposed by the great Swedish chemist Jöns Jakob Berzelius (1779–1848) in 1811.

The elements are shown in a special arrangement, the *periodic table*, at the front of the book and in Table 5-1, and are also given in alphabetical order in the front of the book and in Table 8-1, as well as in the order of their atomic numbers in Table 4-1.

You may find it useful to memorize, at this stage in your study of chemistry, the atomic numbers, names, and symbols of the first eighteen elements.

---

* The word isotope is from the Greek *isos*, the same, and *topos*, place; isotopes occupy the same place in the sequence of elements and in the periodic table (Chapter 5).

TABLE 4-1   *The Names, Atomic Numbers, and Symbols of the Elements*

ATOMIC NUMBER	SYM-BOL	ELEMENT	ATOMIC NUMBER	SYM-BOL	ELEMENT	ATOMIC NUMBER	SYM-BOL	ELEMENT
1	H	Hydrogen	35	Br	Bromine	69	Tm	Thulium
2	He	Helium	36	Kr	Krypton	70	Yb	Ytterbium
3	Li	Lithium	37	Rb	Rubidium	71	Lu	Lutetium
4	Be	Beryllium	38	Sr	Strontium	72	Hf	Hafnium
5	B	Boron	39	Y	Yttrium	73	Ta	Tantalum
6	C	Carbon	40	Zr	Zirconium	74	W	Tungsten
7	N	Nitrogen	41	Nb	Niobium	75	Re	Rhenium
8	O	Oxygen	42	Mo	Molybdenum	76	Os	Osmium
9	F	Fluorine	43	Tc	Technetium	77	Ir	Iridium
10	Ne	Neon	44	Ru	Ruthenium	78	Pt	Platinum
11	Na	Sodium	45	Rh	Rhodium	79	Au	Gold
12	Mg	Magnesium	46	Pd	Palladium	80	Hg	Mercury
13	Al	Aluminum	47	Ag	Silver	81	Tl	Thallium
14	Si	Silicon	48	Cd	Cadmium	82	Pb	Lead
15	P	Phosphorus	49	In	Indium	83	Bi	Bismuth
16	S	Sulfur	50	Sn	Tin	84	Po	Polonium
17	Cl	Chlorine	51	Sb	Antimony	85	At	Astatine
18	A	Argon	52	Te	Tellurium	86	Rn	Radon
19	K	Potassium	53	I	Iodine	87	Fr	Francium
20	Ca	Calcium	54	Xe	Xenon	88	Ra	Radium
21	Sc	Scandium	55	Cs	Cesium	89	Ac	Actinium
22	Ti	Titanium	56	Ba	Barium	90	Th	Thorium
23	V	Vanadium	57	La	Lanthanum	91	Pa	Protactinium
24	Cr	Chromium	58	Ce	Cerium	92	U	Uranium
25	Mn	Manganese	59	Pr	Praseodymium	93	Np	Neptunium
26	Fe	Iron	60	Nd	Neodymium	94	Pu	Plutonium
27	Co	Cobalt	61	Pm	Promethium	95	Am	Americium
28	Ni	Nickel	62	Sm	Samarium	96	Cm	Curium
29	Cu	Copper	63	Eu	Europium	97	Bk	Berkelium
30	Zn	Zinc	64	Gd	Gadolinium	98	Cf	Californium
31	Ga	Gallium	65	Tb	Terbium	99	E	Einsteinium
32	Ge	Germanium	66	Dy	Dysprosium	100	Fm	Fermium
33	As	Arsenic	67	Ho	Holmium	101	Mv	Mendelevium
34	Se	Selenium	68	Er	Erbium			

A symbol is used to represent an atom of an element, as well as the element itself. The symbol I represents the element iodine, and also may be used to mean the elementary substance. However, I_2 is the customary formula for the elementary substance, because it is known that elementary iodine consists of molecules containing two atoms in the solid and liquid states as well as in the gaseous state (except at very high temperature).

Illustrative Exercises

4-1.   The atomic number of oxygen is 8. What is the electric charge on the nucleus of the oxygen atom, in units e? In statcoulombs? How many electrons are there in the oxygen atom? Note that every electrically neutral atom must have a number of electrons around the nucleus equal to the atomic number of the atom; the negative charges of these electrons then exactly neutralize (balance) the total positive charge, $+Ze$, of the nucleus.

4-2. Write from memory the symbols and names of the elements with atomic numbers 1 to 18.

4–2. The Distribution of the Elements

You may be interested to know how the different elements are distributed throughout the earth and the universe.

The structure of the earth, as indicated by the analysis of evidence from records of earthquakes, study of rocks, and other observations, is shown in Figure 4-1. There is an outer crust, about 30 km thick, then an inner shell of denser rock, and a metallic core.

The estimated composition of the outer crust of the earth is shown in Figure 4-5 and the occurrence of the ten most common elements in it is given in Table 4-2.

TABLE 4-2   *The Estimated Composition by Weight of the Earth's Crust**

Oxygen	46.5%	Sodium	3.0%
Silicon	28.0%	Potassium	2.5%
Aluminum	8.1%	Magnesium	2.2%
Iron	5.1%	Titanium	0.5%
Calcium	3.5%	Hydrogen	0.2%

* This is the composition of the solid (rocky) crust of the earth, not including the ocean and the atmosphere. The ocean contains 85.79% oxygen, 10.67% hydrogen, 1.14% sodium, 2.07% chlorine, 0.14% magnesium, and 0.19% other elements.

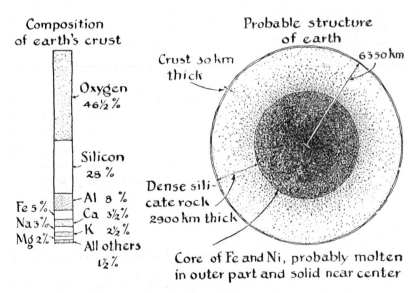

Composition of earth's crust

Oxygen 46½%
Silicon 28%
Fe 5%
Na 3%
Mg 2%
Al 8%
Ca 3½%
K 2½%
All others 1½%

Probable structure of earth

Crust 30 km thick
6350 km

Dense silicate rock 2900 km thick

Core of Fe and Ni, probably molten in outer part and solid near center

FIGURE 4-1   *The composition of the earth's crust.*

In some regions of the earth's surface there are denser rocks that are thought to be like the material in the shell under the earth's crust. On the assumption that the composition of these rocks is the same as the composition of this shell, and that the metallic core of the earth is an iron-nickel alloy resembling the metallic meteorites, the percentages given in Table 4-3 have been calculated for the distribution of elements in the whole earth.

TABLE 4-3   *The Estimated Composition by Weight of the Entire Earth*

Iron	39.8%	Calcium	2.5%
Oxygen	27.7%	Aluminum	1.8%
Silicon	14.5%	Sulfur	0.6%
Magnesium	8.7%	Sodium	0.4%
Nickel	3.2%	All others	0.8%

Astronomers have studied the light from the sun and stars, and have found that the same elements are present in these heavenly bodies as in the earth, but in different relative amounts. The sun and the stars contain great amounts of the two lightest elements, hydrogen and helium, which are relatively rare in the earth.

4–3. *The Formulas of Compounds*

Compounds are represented by formulas. These formulas are made up of the symbols of the elements contained in the compounds. For example, NaCl is the formula for sodium chloride, which consists of equal numbers of sodium and chlorine atoms. When the atoms of the different elements are not present in the compound in equal numbers, their ratios are indicated by the use of subscripts. Thus H_2O is the formula for water, each molecule of which contains two hydrogen atoms and one oxygen atom. (The subscript 1 is not usually written in formulas.)

If the true molecular structure of a substance is known, it is proper to indicate it in the formula. Hydrogen peroxide is a compound of hydrogen and oxygen which differs from water in that two hydrogen atoms and two oxygen atoms are contained in its molecule. The formula for hydrogen peroxide is H_2O_2, and not HO. Similarly the formula for naphthalene (Figure 2-8) is $C_{10}H_8$, and not C_5H_4, because each molecule contains ten carbon atoms and eight hydrogen atoms.

Sometimes parentheses are used in a formula, to indicate how the atoms are grouped together in the molecule or crystal. A subscript to a parenthesis applies to each symbol within the parentheses. For example, the formula $Ca(OH)_2$ means one calcium atom, two oxygen atoms, and two hydrogen atoms. Also, a number may appear in front of a group of symbols; it serves as a factor. For example, borax, $Na_2B_4O_7 \cdot 10H_2O$, consists of ten water molecules (twenty hydrogen atoms and ten oxygen

FIGURE 4-2   *At the left there are represented chlorine gas molecules (Cl_2) and metallic sodium, and at the right the same system after chemical reaction, with the formation of common salt, sodium chloride.*

atoms) in addition to two sodium atoms, four boron atoms, and seven oxygen atoms.

Atomic Ratios in Compounds.   In the crystal of sodium chloride there are atoms of two different kinds, arranged in the regular pattern shown at the right of Figure 4-2. The smaller atoms are those of sodium and the larger ones are those of chlorine. The surface layers shown, which are the cube faces of the sodium chloride crystal, contain both kinds of atoms in equal numbers, when the pattern is repeated a great number of times.

The numerical ratio of sodium and chlorine atoms in solid sodium chloride is fixed at 1:1 by the structure of the crystal, and that for sodium chloride gas is likewise fixed at 1:1 by the structure of the gas molecule, which contains one sodium atom and one chlorine atom. Similarly the numerical ratio of hydrogen atoms and oxygen atoms in water is fixed at 2:1 by the structure of the water molecule. *It is the definite structure of crystals and molecules that causes substances in general to contain elements in definite atomic ratios.*

Illustrative Exercises

4-3.   The formula of ethyl alcohol is C_2H_5OH. What elements are present in this compound? How many atoms of each element are there in one molecule of the compound?

4-4.   The front layer of atoms in the drawing of the crystal of sodium chloride, Figure 4-2, contains four sodium atoms and five chlorine atoms. Show that if this layer were very large (say 1000 atoms on edge) the ratio of the numbers of sodium and chlorine atoms would be very close to 1:1, and not 4:5. (Note that sodium atoms and chlorine atoms alternate in each row.)

4-5. Write the formula for the substance nitric acid; its molecule contains one hydrogen atom, one nitrogen atom, and three oxygen atoms.

4–4. The Atomic and Molecular Nature of Chemical Reactions

In Chapter 1 it was pointed out that a chemical reaction is a process in which certain substances, the reactants, are converted into other substances, the products. We shall now discuss chemical reactions in relation to the atomic theory.

During a **chemical reaction** *there occurs a* **rearrangement of atoms.**

For example, let us consider again the reaction of sodium and chlorine to form sodium chloride. The metal sodium consists of sodium atoms arranged in a regular structure which is similar to that described in Chapter 2 for copper, but is not identical with it. The gas chlorine consists of molecules, as shown in Figure 4-2. During the reaction of sodium and chlorine the sodium atoms in the metal separate from one another and the two chlorine atoms in the molecules of chlorine separate from one another. The atoms of sodium and chlorine then arrange themselves in a new structure, in which the atoms of the two kinds alternate, as shown at the right in Figure 4-2. This arrangement of sodium and chlorine atoms constitutes the new substance, sodium chloride, that has formed during the chemical reaction.

The gas hydrogen consists of molecules H_2. Oxygen also consists of

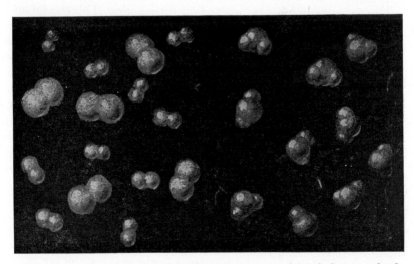

FIGURE 4-3 *At the left there is represented a gas containing hydrogen molecules* (H_2) *and oxygen molecules* (O_2), *and at the right the same system after chemical reaction, leading to the formation of water molecules,* H_2O.

molecules O_2. If two flasks, one containing hydrogen and one containing oxygen, are connected together, the two gases mix with each other quietly, to produce a gaseous mixture (left side of Figure 4-3). If, however, a flame is brought into contact with the gaseous mixture a violent explosion occurs, and afterward the presence of water can be shown. This explosion is the result of the combination of hydrogen and oxygen to form a new substance, water (right side of Figure 4-3), with the emission also of heat and light. During the explosion (which is a very rapid chemical reaction) the molecules of hydrogen and oxygen split into atoms, and two atoms of hydrogen attach themselves to each atom of oxygen, to form molecules of water, H_2O.

4–5. *How to Balance the Equation for a Chemical Reaction*

The chemical reaction of the formation of water from hydrogen and oxygen can be represented by an equation:

$$2H_2 + O_2 \longrightarrow 2H_2O$$

On the left side of this equation we have the formula H_2 for hydrogen and the formula O_2 for oxygen, and on the right side the formula H_2O for water. It would not, however, be correct to write this equation without the numerical prefixes that are indicated, because we use the formulas to indicate relative numbers of atoms, as well as to describe the reactants and the products of the chemical reaction. The water molecule contains twice as many hydrogen atoms as oxygen atoms, and accordingly the equation should show that twice as many hydrogen atoms as oxygen atoms are needed for the reaction. This can be achieved by introducing the coefficient (multiplier) 2 in front of the symbol for the hydrogen molecule. If four hydrogen atoms (two molecules) and two oxygen atoms (one molecule) react, two water molecules are formed. This is indicated by use of the coefficient 2 in front of the formula for water.

The coefficient 2 in the term $2H_2$ means that two molecules of hydrogen, four hydrogen atoms altogether, are involved in the reaction. The coefficient 2 in the term $2H_2O$ multiplies the entire formula H_2O; that is, $2H_2O$ means two molecules H_2O (four hydrogen atoms and two oxygen atoms).

Note that it is customary to use an arrow in a chemical equation, rather than the mathematical sign of equality.

The equation representing a chemical reaction can thus be written correctly by carrying out a process of **balancing the equation.** This is done by introducing numerical coefficients before the correct formulas of the reactants and products until there are exactly the same number of atoms of each element on the left side of the equation as on the right side of the equation.

The equation representing the reaction in which sodium chloride is formed from sodium and chlorine may be easily written. It is

$$2Na + Cl_2 \longrightarrow 2NaCl$$

It is a very good practice to check every chemical equation that you write, to be sure that it agrees with the **"law of the conservation of atoms of every element."**

Illustrative Exercises

4-6. (a) How many atoms of hydrogen and how many atoms of oxygen are there in 100 molecules of water? (b) How many molecules of hydrogen and how many molecules of oxygen would be required to produce 100 molecules of water? (c) Write the equation for the reaction, with 100 H_2O as the product. (d) Reduce this equation to its simplest form, by dividing by the greatest common divisor of the coefficients of the three terms.

4-7. Hydrogen peroxide, H_2O_2, easily decomposes into water and oxygen. Write a balanced equation for this reaction.

4-8. Balance the following equations (the formulas are correct):

$H_2 + Cl_2 \longrightarrow HCl$

$K + I_2 \longrightarrow KI$

$Fe + H_2SO_4 \longrightarrow FeSO_4 + H_2$

$C_{10}H_8 + O_2 \longrightarrow CO_2 + H_2O$

$C_6H_{14} + O_2 \longrightarrow CO_2 + H_2O$

$C_6H_{14} + O_2 \longrightarrow CO + H_2O$

$H_2O_2 \longrightarrow H_2O + O_2$

$C_2H_5OH + O_2 \longrightarrow CO_2 + H_2O$

$AgNO_3 + CaCl_2 \longrightarrow AgCl + Ca(NO_3)_2$

$Al + O_2 \longrightarrow Al_2O_3$

4–6. The Difference in Chemical Properties of Elements and Compounds

It is only recently that methods have become available for determining directly whether a substance contains atoms of only one kind or of two or more kinds. For two hundred years, since 1741, when M. V. Lomonosov (1711–1765), an imaginative Russian poet and chemist, published his new ideas about the nature of matter, and especially since 1789, when Lavoisier published such a clear discussion of the question as to convince nearly all of his fellow chemists, substances had undergone classification as elements or compounds on the basis of chemical reactions, as was briefly discussed in Chapter 1. Definite chemical evidence for the compound nature of a substance could be obtained, by decomposing it into two or more substances; if it was lacking, the substance was presumed to be an element.

There are two chemical tests for the compound nature of a substance.

First: if a substance can be decomposed (that is, if it can be made to undergo reaction in which it alone is destroyed) to form two or more product substances,* the original substance must be a compound. For example, molten salt can be decomposed completely into sodium and chlorine by passing an electric current through it; hence it is a compound. Similarly, mercuric oxide, HgO, can be decomposed into mercury and oxygen simply by heating it; hence it is a compound.

The second chemical test for the compound nature of a substance is the following: if two or more substances react to form a single product substance, that substance is a compound. Thus sodium and chlorine, in the proper relative amounts, will react completely to form common salt; hence common salt is a compound. Also hydrogen and oxygen mixed in the proper proportions will explode to form a single substance, water; hence water is a compound.

It is interesting to note that *until the new physical methods, especially the x-ray method* (Section 4–8), *were developed, there was no way of rigorously proving a substance to be an element.* In the early years of the science of chemistry a substance was accepted as an element so long as no reaction showing it to be a compound had been observed. At first some mistakes were made: lime (calcium oxide, CaO) was considered to be an element until the English chemist Sir Humphry Davy reduced it to calcium metal in 1808; and uranium dioxide, UO_2, was accepted as an element from 1789 to 1841. By 1900, however, all but about a score of the elements that are now known had been recognized and correctly identified as elements.

This chemical method of classifying substances is interesting as an example of logical argument. A *single experiment* in which a substance is decomposed into two or more other substances or is alone formed from them *proves* that it is a compound; this conclusion is inescapable. The *failure* of such an experiment, however, *does not prove* that the substance is an element. It is, indeed, not possible to prove that a substance is an element by tests of this kind, no matter how many are made. It may be convenient to assume it to be an element, in case that there is no evidence to the contrary; but if this is done it should not be forgotten that the assumption is not necessarily true.

It was not until the present century, when powerful methods of studying atoms were discovered, that scientists could be sure that the forms of matter which they called elements were all really elements, and that some were not compounds.

* Here it is assumed that the different products are essentially different, and do not contain the same atoms (as do oxygen and ozone, Chapter 6).

4–7. *Note on Radioactivity and the Transmutation of Elements*

For centuries, before the development of chemistry as a science, the alchemists strove to carry out the transmutation of elements, in particular to change mercury into gold with the aid of the "philosopher's stone." Then, as scientific chemistry developed and success in transmutation eluded the investigators, the opinion gained firm hold that the conversion of one element into another was impossible, and that atoms were immutable and indestructible. The definitions of element and elementary substance accepted during the nineteenth century were based upon this belief.

In 1896 there came the discovery of radioactivity by Henri Becquerel and the discovery of radium by Pierre and Marie Curie. Soon thereafter it was recognized that *radioactive changes involve the spontaneous conversion of atoms of one element into those of another.* It then became necessary to change the definition of element; this was done by saying that one element could not be converted into another *by artificial means.*

It has now become necessary to make another change in the definition. In 1919 Lord Rutherford and his collaborators at the Cavendish Laboratory in Cambridge, England, where active study of radioactive phenomena was under way, reported that they had succeeded in converting nitrogen atoms into oxygen atoms by bombarding nitrogen with high-speed alpha particles, which are given off by radium. The nitrogen nucleus, with charge $+7e$, and the alpha particle (helium nucleus), with charge $+2e$, react to produce an oxygen nucleus, with charge $+8e$, and a proton, with charge $+e$.

Since 1930 there has been very great progress in this field of artificial radioactivity, which now is the most actively prosecuted research field in physics. Nearly every element has now been rendered radioactive and converted into other elements by bombardment with particles moving at high speed, and a great body of information about the properties of atomic nuclei is being gathered.

These developments necessitate another change in the concept of element: it is now said that *an element cannot be transmuted into another element by ordinary chemical methods.* The discovery of these new phenomena might have led to confusion regarding the validity of the classification of substances as elementary substances and compounds were it not for the fact that our knowledge of the structure and properties of atoms has also increased rapidly in recent years.

4–8. *Moseley's Experiment*

It was mentioned in Section 4–1 that Moseley determined the atomic numbers of elements by the study of the x-rays emitted by an x-ray tube containing the element. The

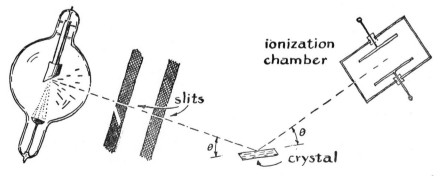

FIGURE 4-4   *The Bragg ionization-chamber technique of investigating the diffraction of x-rays by crystals.*

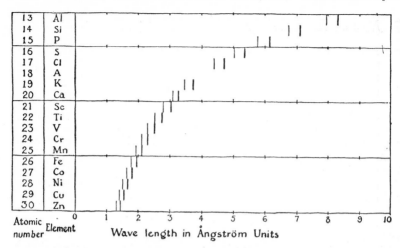

FIGURE 4-5   *Diagram showing regular change of wavelength of x-ray emission lines for a series of elements.*

apparatus that might be used to repeat Moseley's experiment is shown in Figure 4-4. The x-ray tube is drawn at the left side of this figure. Electrons that come from the cup near the bottom of the tube (as drawn) are speeded up by the electric potential (several thousand volts) applied to the two ends of the tube, and strike the target, which is near the center of the tube. The x-rays are emitted by the atoms of the target, when they are struck by the fast-moving electrons.

The element to be investigated is placed on the target of the x-ray tube, and the x-rays that it emits when bombarded by electrons are then analyzed by a technique developed in 1913 by Sir William Bragg (1862–1942) and his son, Sir Lawrence Bragg (born 1890). This consists in defining a beam of x-rays by a pair of slits, reflecting the beam of x-rays from the face of a crystal, as shown in Figure 4-4, and determining the position of the reflected beam either by use of an ionization chamber (a chamber in which the x-rays cause a gas to become a conductor of electricity), as indicated in the figure, or by use of a photographic plate.

It was found that the x-rays produced by an x-ray tube contain lines of definite wavelengths, characteristic of the material in the target of the x-ray tube. Moseley measured the wavelengths produced by a number of different elements, and found that they change in a regular way. The wavelengths of the two principal x-ray lines of the elements from aluminum to zinc (omitting the gas argon) are shown in Figure 4-5.

The regularity in the wavelengths can be shown more strikingly by plotting the square root of the reciprocals of the wavelengths of the two x-ray lines for the various elements arranged in the proper sequence, which is the sequence of the atomic numbers of the elements. In a graph of this sort, called a Moseley diagram, the points for a given x-ray line lie on a straight line. The Moseley diagram for the elements from aluminum to zinc is shown in Figure 4-6. It was easy for Moseley to assign the correct atomic numbers to the elements with use of a diagram of this sort.

Concepts and Technical Terms Introduced in This Chapter

Element—the kind of matter represented by atoms with the same atomic number.

Atomic number—the magnitude of the positive electric charge of the nucleus of an atom (in units equal to the charge of the electron).

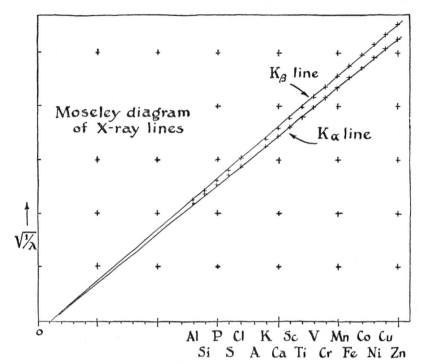

FIGURE 4-6 *A graph of the reciprocal of the square root of the wavelengths of x-ray lines, for the K_α line and the K_β line, of elements, plotted against the order of the elements in the periodic table. This graph, called the Moseley diagram, was used by Moseley in determining the atomic numbers of the elements.*

Elementary substance—a substance containing atoms of one kind only.

Compound—a substance containing two or more kinds of atoms in a definite ratio.

Isotopes.

The 101 elements, their names and symbols.

Distribution of elements.

Chemical formulas.

Chemical reactions, their atomic and molecular nature.

How to balance equations.

Difference in chemical properties of elements and compounds.

Radioactivity and the transmutation of elements.

Moseley's experiment, determining values of atomic numbers.

Exercises

4-9.   Define atomic number. Define elementary substance in terms of atoms.

4-10.   Describe a chemical experiment which would prove that water is not an element. Can you think of a chemical proof that iron is an element?

4-11. When sugar is strongly heated water vapor is driven off and a black residue, carbon, is left. Does this experiment prove rigorously that sugar is not an element?

4-12. Define chemical symbol and chemical formula. Explain the purpose of each letter or number in a formula.

4-13. Using your own words, give a definition of chemical reaction.

4-14. Balance the following equations of chemical reactions:

$$Fe + O_2 \longrightarrow Fe_2O_3$$

$$H_2 + N_2 \longrightarrow NH_3$$

$$HgO \longrightarrow Hg + O_2$$

$$CO + O_2 \longrightarrow CO_2$$

$$C_{12}H_{22}O_{11} + O_2 \longrightarrow CO_2 + H_2O$$

$$NaCl + H_2SO_4 \longrightarrow NaHSO_4 + HCl$$

$$KClO_3 \longrightarrow KCl + O_2$$

$$H_2 + O_2 \longrightarrow H_2O$$

$$Zn + H_2SO_4 \longrightarrow ZnSO_4 + H_2$$

4-15. How was the definition of element affected by the discovery of radioactivity in 1896?

4-16. What are the atomic number and approximate atomic weight of the element each of whose nuclei contains 79 protons and 118 neutrons? By reference to Table 4-1 identify this element.

4-17. How many protons and how many neutrons are in the nucleus of the isotope of chlorine with mass 35? Of the isotope of chlorine with mass 37? Of the isotope of plutonium with mass 239?

Reference Books

F. Sherwood Taylor, *The Alchemists*, Henry Schuman, 1948.

J. Newton Friend, *Man and the Chemical Elements*, Charles Griffin & Co., London, 1951.

Also the books listed at the end of Chapter 1, especially *Discovery of the Elements*, by Mary E. Weeks.

Chapter 5

The Chemical Elements, the Periodic Law, and the Electronic Structure of Atoms

The 101 known elements include some with which everyone is familiar and many which are rare. At room temperature some of the elementary substances are gases, some are liquids, and some are solids.* They show extremely great variety in their chemical properties and in the nature of the compounds that they form. In consequence the study of chemistry is not simple or easy; to obtain a reasonably broad knowledge of general chemistry it is necessary to learn a great many facts.

The facts of chemistry cannot be completely coordinated by a unifying theory. Nevertheless, the development of chemical theories has now proceeded far enough to be of great aid to the student, who can simplify his task of learning about the properties and reactions of substances by correlating this information with theories, such as the theory of atomic structure,† which has been discussed in the preceding chapters, and the *periodic law*, which we shall now consider.

---

* The elements that are gases at standard conditions (0°C and 1 atm) are hydrogen, helium, nitrogen, oxygen, fluorine, neon, chlorine, argon, krypton, xenon, and radon. The only elements that are liquids at standard conditions are bromine and mercury.

† Remember that atoms are built of particles of three kinds, protons, neutrons, and electrons. The nucleus of the atom is made of protons and neutrons; the number of protons determines its electric charge, and the total number of protons and neutrons its mass. The number of electrons around the nucleus equals the number of protons in it.

5–1. *The Periodic Law*

The periodic law states simply that *the properties of the chemical elements are not arbitrary, but depend upon the structure of the atom and vary with the atomic number in a systematic way.* The important point is that this dependence involves a crude periodicity which shows itself in the recurrence of characteristic properties.

For example, the elements with atomic numbers 2, 10, 18, 36, 54, and 86 are all chemically inert gases. Similarly the elements with atomic numbers one greater, namely, 3, 11, 19, 37, 55, and 87, are all light metals that are very reactive chemically. These six metals, lithium (3), sodium (11), potassium (19), rubidium (37), cesium (55), and francium (87), all react with chlorine to form colorless compounds that crystallize in cubes and show a cubic cleavage. The chemical formulas of these salts are similar: $LiCl$, $NaCl$, KCl, $RbCl$, $CsCl$, and $FrCl$. The composition and properties of other compounds of these six metals are correspondingly similar, and different from those of other elements.*

The comparison of the observed chemical and physical properties of elements and their compounds with the atomic numbers of the elements accordingly indicates that, after the first two elements, hydrogen and helium, which constitute the **very short period** (the word period is used for a sequence of elements), there are the **first short period** of eight elements (from helium, atomic number 2, to neon, 10), the **second short period** of eight elements (to argon, 18), the **first long period** of eighteen elements (to krypton, 36), the **second long period** of eighteen elements (to xenon, 54), and then the **very long period** of 32 elements (to radon, 86). In case that enough new elements of very large atomic number are made in the future it may well be found that there is another very long period of 32 elements, ending in another inert gas, with atomic number 118.

5–2. *The Periodic Table*

The periodic recurrence of properties of the elements with increasing atomic number may be effectively emphasized by arranging the elements in a table, called the *periodic table* or *periodic system* of the elements. Several alternative forms of the periodic table have been proposed and used. We shall base the discussion of the elements and their properties in this book on the simple table shown as Table 5-1 (it is also reproduced inside the front cover of the book).

---

* Actually very little is yet known about the sixth of these elements, francium, which has been only recently discovered; but there is little doubt that francium is closely similar to the other alkali metals in its properties. We say "little doubt" because *periodicity* has in the past consistently permitted chemists to make such predictions that have later been proved to be correct.

TABLE 5–1

Group O	
H 1	He 2

Short periods:

O	I	II	III	IV	V	VI	VII	O
								He 2
	Li 3	Be 4	B 5	C 6	N 7	O 8	F 9	Ne 10
	Na 11	Mg 12	Al 13	Si 14	P 15	S 16	Cl 17	A 18

Long periods:

O	I	II	III	IVa	Va	VIa	VIIa	VIII			Ib	IIb	IIIb	IV	V	VI	VII	O
A 18	K 19	Ca 20	Sc 21	Ti 22	V 23	Cr 24	Mn 25	Fe 26	Co 27	Ni 28	Cu 29	Zn 30	Ga 31	Ge 32	As 33	Se 34	Br 35	Kr 36
Kr 36	Rb 37	Sr 38	Y 39	Zr 40	Nb 41	Mo 42	Tc 43	Ru 44	Rh 45	Pd 46	Ag 47	Cd 48	In 49	Sn 50	Sb 51	Te 52	I 53	Xe 54
Xe 54	Cs 55	Ba 56	La 57 *	Hf 72	Ta 73	W 74	Re 75	Os 76	Ir 77	Pt 78	Au 79	Hg 80	Tl 81	Pb 82	Bi 83	Po 84	At 85	Rn 86
Rn 86	Fr 87	Ra 88	Ac 89 ◆	Th 90	Pa 91	U 92	Np 93	Pu 94										

* Lanthanons

Ce 58	Pr 59	Nd 60	Pm 61	Sm 62	Eu 63	Gd 64	Tb 65	Dy 66	Ho 67	Er 68	Tm 69	Yb 70	Lu 71

◆ Actinons

Th 90	Pa 91	U 92	Np 93	Pu 94	Am 95	Cm 96	Bk 97	Cf 98	E 99	Fm 100	Mv 101

The Development of the Periodic Table. The differentiation of chemical substances into two groups, elements and compounds, was achieved at the end of the eighteenth century. A long time was required for the recognition of the fact that the elements can be classified in the way now described by the periodic law. The first step was taken in 1817, when the German chemist J. W. Döbereiner (1780–1849) showed that the combining weight of strontium lies midway between the combining weights of the two related elements calcium and barium. Some years later he recognized the existence of other "triads" of similar elements (chlorine, bromine, and iodine; lithium, sodium, and potassium).

Other chemists then showed that the elements could be classified into groups consisting of more than three similar elements. Fluorine was added to the triad chlorine, bromine, and iodine, and magnesium to the triad calcium, strontium, and barium. Oxygen, sulfur, selenium, and tellurium had been classed as one group, and nitrogen, phosphorus, arsenic, antimony, and bismuth as another group of elements by 1854.

In 1862 the French chemist A. E. B. de Chancourtois arranged the elements in the order of atomic weights (the masses of their atoms). He noticed that elements differing by about 16 in atomic weight sometimes had similar properties, and suggested that "the properties of elements are the properties of numbers." The English chemist J. A. R. Newlands in 1863 proposed a system of classification of the elements in order of atomic weights, in which the elements were divided into seven groups of seven elements each. He termed his relation the *law of octaves*, by analogy with the seven intervals of the musical scale. His proposal was ridiculed, however, and he did not develop it further.

The most important step in the development of the periodic table was taken in 1869, when the Russian chemist Dmitri I. Mendelyeev (1834–1907) made a thorough study of the relation between the atomic weights of the elements and their physical and chemical properties. Mendelyeev proposed a periodic table containing seventeen columns, resembling in a general way the periodic Table 5-1 with the end columns (labeled 0) missing (these elements had not yet been discovered at that time). In 1871 Mendelyeev and the German chemist Lothar Meyer (1830–1895), who was working independently, proposed another table, with eight columns, obtained by splitting each of the long periods into a period of seven elements, an eighth group containing the three central elements (such as Fe, Co, Ni), and a second period of seven elements. The first and second periods of seven were later distinguished by use of the letters a and b attached to the group symbols, which were the Roman numerals. This nomenclature of the periods (Ia, IIa, IIIa, IVa, Va, VIa, VIIa, VIII, Ib, IIb, IIIb, IVb, Vb, VIb, VIIb) appears, slightly revised, in the present periodic table.

The periodic table in the second form proposed by Mendelyeev (the "short-period" form) remained popular for many years, but has now been largely replaced by the "long-period" form, used in this book, which is in better agreement with the new knowledge about the electronic structure of atoms.

The periodic law was accepted immediately after its proposal by Mendelyeev because of his success in making predictions with its use which were afterward verified by experiment. In 1871 Mendelyeev found that by changing seventeen elements from the positions indicated by the atomic weights which had then been assigned to them into new positions, their properties could be better correlated with the properties of the other elements. He pointed out that this change indicated the existence of small errors in the previously accepted atomic weights of several of the elements, and large errors for several others, to the compounds of which incorrect formulas had been assigned. Further experimental work verified that Mendelyeev's revisions were correct.

A very striking application of the periodic law was made by Mendelyeev. He was able to predict the existence of six elements that had not yet been discovered, corresponding to vacant places in his table. He named these elements eka-boron, eka-aluminum, eka-silicon, eka-manganese, dvi-manganese, and eka-tantalum (Sanskrit: *eka*, first; *dvi*, second).

Three of these elements were soon discovered (they were named scandium, gallium, and germanium by their discoverers), and it was found that their properties and the properties of their compounds are very close to those predicted by Mendelyeev for eka-boron, eka-aluminum, and eka-silicon, respectively. Since then the elements technetium, rhenium, and protactinium have been discovered or made artificially, and have been found to have properties similar to those predicted for eka-manganese, dvi-manganese, and eka-tantalum. A comparison of the properties predicted by Mendelyeev for eka-silicon and those determined experimentally for germanium is given below:

Mendelyeev's predictions for eka-silicon (1871):	*Observed properties of germanium (discovered in 1886):*
Atomic weight about 72.	Atomic weight 72.60.
Es will be obtained from EsO_2 or K_2EsF_6 by reaction with sodium.	Ge is obtained by reaction of K_2GeF_6 and sodium.
Es will be a dark gray metal, with high melting point and density 5.5.	Ge is gray, with melting point 958° C and density 5.36 g/cm³.
Es will be slightly attacked by acids, such as hydrochloric acid, HCl, and will resist alkalies, such as sodium hydroxide, NaOH.	Ge is not dissolved by HCl or NaOH, but is dissolved by concentrated nitric acid, HNO_3.
On heating Es, it will form the oxide EsO_2, with high melting point and density 4.7.	Ge reacts with oxygen to give GeO_2, m.p. 1100° C, density 4.70 g/cm³.
A hydrated EsO_2 soluble in acid and easily reprecipitated is expected.	$Ge(OH)_4$ dissolves in dilute acid and is reprecipitated on dilution or addition of base.
The sulfide, EsS_2, will be insoluble in water but soluble in ammonium sulfide.	GeS_2 is insoluble in water and dilute acids, but readily soluble in ammonium sulfide.
$EsCl_4$ will be a volatile liquid, with boiling point a little under 100° and density 1.9 g/cm³.	$GeCl_4$ is a volatile liquid, with b.p. 83° C and density 1.88 g/cm³.

5–3. *Description of the Periodic Table*

The **horizontal rows** *of the periodic table are called* **periods:** they consist of a very short period (containing hydrogen and helium, atomic numbers 1 and 2), two short periods of 8 elements each, two long periods of 18 elements each, a very long period of 32 elements, and an incomplete period.

The properties of elements change in a systematic way through a period: this is indicated in Figure 5-1, which shows the density of the elements, in the crystalline state, as a function of the atomic number. It is seen that there are five pronounced minima (low points) in the density curve. They occur for the elements sodium (11), potassium (19), rubidium (37), cesium (55), and francium (87). It was mentioned in Section 5–1 that these five elements together with lithium constitute a group of elements that are strikingly similar in their properties.

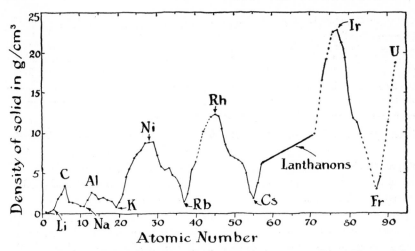

FIGURE 5-1   *The density of the elements in the solid state, in g/cm³. The symbols of the elements at high and low points of the jagged curve are shown.*

The **vertical columns** *of the periodic table,* with connections between the short and long periods as shown, *are the* **groups** *of chemical elements.* Elements in the same group may be called *congeners;* these elements have closely related physical and chemical properties.

The groups I, II, and III are considered to include the elements in corresponding places at the left side of all the periods in Table 5-1, and IV, V, VI, and VII the elements at the right side. The central elements of the long periods, called the *transition elements,* have properties differing from those of the elements of the short periods; these elements are discussed separately, as groups IVa, Va, VIa, VIIa, VIII (which, for historical reasons, include three elements in each long period), Ib, IIb, and IIIb.

The very long period is compressed into the table by removing fourteen elements, the *rare-earth metals* or *lanthanons* (elements resembling lanthanum, $Z = 57$), from $Z = 58$ to $Z = 71$, and representing them separately below. The elements from $Z = 90$ to $Z = 101$, called the *actinons** (elements resembling actinium, $Z = 89$), are listed below the lanthanons; those from $Z = 90$ to $Z = 94$ are also listed in the main body of the table.

The elements on the left side and in the center of the periodic table are **metals.** These elementary substances have the characteristic properties called *metallic properties*—high electric and thermal conductivity, metallic luster, the ability to be hammered into sheets (malleability) and to be drawn into wire (ductility). The elements on the right side

---

* There should be fourteen actinons ($Z = 90$ to $Z = 103$), but the last two have not yet been made.

of the periodic table are **non-metals,** the elementary substances not having metallic properties.

The metallic properties are most pronounced for elements in the lower left-hand corner of the periodic table, and the non-metallic properties are most pronounced for elements in the upper right-hand corner. The transition from metals to non-metals is marked by the *elements with intermediate properties*, which occupy a diagonal region extending from a point near the upper center to the lower right-hand corner. These elements, which are called **metalloids,** include boron, silicon, germanium, arsenic, antimony, tellurium, and polonium.

The groups of elements may be described briefly in the following way :

Group 0, the noble gases: The elements of this group, helium, neon, argon, krypton, xenon, and radon, are completely unreactive chemically; they do not form any chemical compounds. A discussion of the noble gases is given in the following sections of this chapter.

Group I, the alkali metals: the alkali metals, lithium, sodium, potassium, rubidium, cesium, and francium, are light metals which are very reactive chemically. Many of their compounds have important uses in industry and in life. The alkali metals and their compounds are discussed in Chapter 26. The word alkali is derived from an arabic word meaning ashes (compounds of these metals were obtained from wood ashes).

Group II, the alkaline-earth metals: These metals, beryllium, magnesium, calcium, strontium, barium, and radium, and their compounds are discussed in Chapter 26.

Group III, the boron or aluminum group: Boron is a metalloid, whereas aluminum and its other congeners are metals. The properties of boron and its congeners are discussed in Chapter 26.

Group IV, carbon and silicon: The chemistry of carbon is described in Chapter 7 and in greater detail in Chapters 30 and 31. The chemistry of silicon and the other elements of this group is described in Chapter 26.

Group V, the nitrogen or phosphorus group: Nitrogen and phosphorus are non-metals, their congeners arsenic and antimony are metalloids, and bismuth is usually classed as a metal. The chemistry of nitrogen is described in Chapter 15 and that of phosphorus and the other elements of the group in Chapter 16.

Group VI, the oxygen group: Oxygen and its congeners sulfur and selenium are non-metals, whereas tellurium and polonium are classed as metalloids. The chemistry of oxygen is discussed in Chapter 6, and that of sulfur and its congeners in Chapter 14.

Group VII, the halogen group: The halogens (fluorine, chlorine, bromine, iodine, and astatine) are the most strongly non-metallic elements. They are very reactive chemically, and form many compounds. Their chemistry is discussed in Chapter 13. The word halogen is from the Greek words *hals*, salt, and *genes*, producing.

Groups IVa, Va, VIa, VIIa, VIII, Ib, IIb, and IIIb, the transition elements: The elements in these groups are all metals. The groups themselves are usually given the name of the lightest metal; for example, VIa, including chromium, molybdenum, tungsten, and uranium, is called the chromium group. For historical reasons, however, the iron group is often considered to consist of three elements, iron, cobalt, and nickel, the congeners of these three elements being called the platinum group. These elements are discussed in later chapters of the book: iron, cobalt, nickel, and the platinum metals in Chapter 27; copper, zinc, gallium, and their congeners in Chapter 28; and chromium and manganese and related metals in Chapter 29.

You will avoid confusion in your further study if you fix firmly in your mind the usage of the word *period* to represent a *horizontal row* in the periodic table, and of the word *group* to represent a *vertical column* (with a jog between the short-period and the long-period part of the table). Also, you will find it helpful to remember the important sequence of numbers 2, 8, 8, 18, 18, 32, 32. These are the numbers of elements in the successive periods of the periodic table. (The last period, which is incomplete, will presumably be found, when more elements are made, to end with another noble gas with $Z = 118$.)

5–4. *The Noble Gases*

The first element in the periodic table, hydrogen, with atomic number 1, is a reactive substance that forms a great many compounds. The chemistry of hydrogen is discussed in the following chapter. Helium, the second element (atomic number 2), is much different; it is a gas with the very striking chemical property that *it forms no chemical compounds whatever*, but exists only in the free state. Its atoms will not even combine with one another to form polyatomic molecules, but remain as separate atoms in the gas, which is hence described as containing monatomic molecules. Because of its property of remaining aloof from other elements it is called a "noble" gas.

This lack of chemical reactivity is the result of an extraordinary stability of the electronic structure of the helium atom. This stability is characteristic of the presence of two electrons close to an atomic nucleus.

The other elements of the zero group—neon, argon, krypton, xenon, and radon—are also chemically inert. The failure of these inert elements to form chemical compounds is similarly due to the great stability of their electronic structures. These extremely stable electronic structures are formed by 2, 10, 18, 36, 54, and 86 electrons about a nucleus.

These six gases are called the *noble gases* (or sometimes the *rare gases* or *inert gases*). Their names, except radon, are from Greek roots: *helios*, sun; *neos*, new; *argos*, inert; *kryptos*, hidden; *xenos*, stranger. Radon is named after radium, from which it is formed by radioactive decomposition. The properties of the noble gases are given in Table 5-2. Note the regular dependence of melting point and boiling point on atomic number.

Helium.   Helium is present in very small quantities in the atmosphere. Its presence in the sun is shown by the occurrence of its spectral lines in sunlight. These lines were observed in 1868, long before the element was discovered on earth, and the lines were ascribed to a new element, which was named helium* by Sir Norman Lockyer (1836–1920).

TABLE 5-2   *Properties of the Noble Gases*

	SYMBOL	ATOMIC NUMBER	ATOMIC WEIGHT*	MELTING POINT	BOILING POINT
Helium	He	2	4.003	−272.2° C†	−268.9° C
Neon	Ne	10	20.183	−248.67°	−245.9°
Argon	A	18	39.944	−189.2°	−185.7°
Krypton	Kr	36	83.80	−157°	−152.9°
Xenon	Xe	54	131.30	−112°	−107.1°
Radon	Rn	86	222	−71°	−61.8°

* See Chapter 8.
† At 26 atm pressure. At smaller pressures helium remains liquid at still lower temperatures.

Helium occurs as a gas entrapped in some uranium minerals, from which it can be liberated by heating. It is also present in natural gas from some wells, especially in Texas and Canada; this is the principal source of the element.

Helium is used for filling balloons and dirigibles and for mixing with oxygen (in place of the nitrogen of the air) for breathing by divers, in order to avoid the "bends," which are caused by gas bubbles formed by release of the nitrogen of the atmosphere that had dissolved in the blood under increased pressure.

Neon.   The second noble gas, neon, occurs in the atmosphere to the extent of 0.002%. It is obtained, along with the other noble gases (except helium), by the distillation of liquid air (air that has been liquefied by cooling).

When an electric current is passed through a tube containing neon gas at low pressure, the atoms of neon are caused to emit light with their characteristic spectral lines. This produces a brilliant red light, used in advertising signs (neon signs). Other colors for signs are obtained by

* The ending "ium," which is otherwise used only for metallic elements, is due to Lockyer's incorrect surmise that the new element was a metal. "Helion" would be a better name, as its ending is consistent with those of the names of the other noble gases.

the use of helium, argon, and mercury, sometimes in mixtures with neon or with one another.

Argon. Argon composes about 1% of the atmosphere. It is used in incandescent light bulbs to permit the filament to be heated to a higher temperature, and thus to produce a whiter light than would be practical in a vacuum. The argon decreases the rate at which the metallic filament evaporates, by keeping vaporized metal atoms from diffusing away from the filament, and permitting them to reattach themselves to it.

Krypton, Xenon, and Radon. Krypton and xenon, which occur in very small quantities in the air, have not found any significant use. Radon, which is produced steadily by radium, is used in the treatment of cancer. It has been found that the rays given off by radioactive substances are often effective in controlling this disease. A convenient way of administering this radiation is to pump the radon that has been produced by a sample of radium into a small gold tube, which is then placed in proximity to the tissues to be treated.*

The Discovery of the Noble Gases. The story of the discovery of argon provides an interesting illustration of the importance of attention to minor discrepancies in the results of scientific investigations.

For over a hundred years it was thought that atmospheric air consisted, aside from small variable amounts of water vapor and carbon dioxide, solely of oxygen (21%

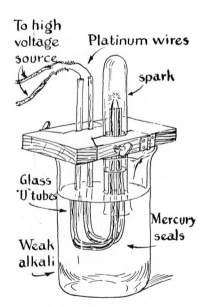

To high voltage source

Platinum wires

spark

Glass "U" tubes

Mercury seals

Weak alkali

FIGURE 5-2

The Cavendish apparatus, used in the investigation of the composition of air.

* Radon is chemically unreactive, but its *nuclei* decompose; see Chapter 32.

by volume) and nitrogen (79%). In 1785 the English 'scientist Henry Cavendish (1731–1810) investigated the composition of the atmosphere. He mixed oxygen with air, and then passed an electric spark through the mixture, to form a compound of nitrogen and oxygen, which was dissolved in a solution in contact with the gas (Figure 5-2). The sparking was continued until there was no further decrease in volume, and the oxygen was then removed from the residual gas by treatment with another solution. He found that after this treatment only a small bubble of air remained unabsorbed, not more than $\frac{1}{120}$ of the original air. Although Lord Cavendish did not commit himself on the point, it seems to have been assumed by chemists that if the sparking had been continued for a longer time there would have been no residue, and Cavendish's experiment was accordingly interpreted as showing that only oxygen and nitrogen were present in the atmosphere.

Then in 1894, more than 100 years later, Lord Rayleigh began an investigation involving the careful determination of the densities of the gases hydrogen, oxygen, and nitrogen. To prepare nitrogen he mixed dried air with an excess of ammonia, NH_3, and passed the mixture over red-hot copper. Under these conditions the oxygen reacts with ammonia, according to the equation

$$4NH_3 + 3O_2 \longrightarrow 6H_2O + 2N_2$$

The excess ammonia is then removed by bubbling the gas through sulfuric acid. The remaining gas, after drying, should have been pure nitrogen, derived in part from the ammonia and in part from air. The density of this gas was determined. Another sample of nitrogen was made simply by passing air over red-hot copper, which removed the oxygen by combining with it to form copper oxide:

$$O_2 + 2Cu \longrightarrow 2CuO$$

When the density of this gas was determined it was found to be about 0.1% greater than that from the sample of ammonia and air. In order to investigate this discrepancy, a third sample of nitrogen was made, by use of a mixture of ammonia and pure oxygen. It was found that this sample of nitrogen had a density 0.5% less than that of the second sample.

Further investigations showed that nitrogen prepared entirely from air had a density 0.5% greater than nitrogen prepared completely from ammonia or in any other chemical way. Nitrogen obtained from air was found to have density 1.2572 g/l at 0° C and 1 atm, whereas nitrogen made by chemical methods had a density 1.2505 g/l. Rayleigh and Ramsay then repeated Cavendish's experiments, and showed by spectroscopic analysis that the residual gas was indeed not nitrogen but a new element. They then searched for the other noble gases and discovered them.

5–5. *The Electronic Structure of Atoms*

The noble gases are strange elements. They are different from all other elements—they do not form any compounds, whereas every other element forms many compounds.

This peculiarity of the noble gases is explained by the **electronic structure** of the noble-gas atoms—the way in which the electrons move about the atomic nuclei. This is the subject that we shall now consider, beginning with the electronic structure of the simplest element, hydrogen.

The knowledge about the structure of atoms that is presented in the following paragraphs has been obtained largely by physicists from the study of spectral lines, that is, study of the light waves with different wavelengths that are emitted by gases which are strongly heated or subjected to the action of an electric current. The understanding of atomic structure was obtained during the years between 1913 and 1925. It was in 1913 that Niels Bohr (born 1885), the great Danish physicist, developed his simple theory of the hydrogen atom, which during the following twelve years was expanded and refined into our present theory of atomic structure.

The detailed mathematical theory of quantum mechanics, the modern mathematical theory of the properties of electrons and other small particles, is not suited to study by the beginning student. However, the picture of the electronic structure of atoms that is provided by this theory is easy to understand and to learn. Knowledge of this electronic structure is important to the student of chemistry.

The Electronic Structure of the Hydrogen Atom. The smallest and lightest nucleus is the proton. The proton carries one unit of positive charge, and with one electron, which carries one unit of negative charge, it forms a hydrogen atom.

Soon after the development of the concept of the nuclear atom, some idea was gained as to the way in which a proton and an electron are combined to form a hydrogen atom. Because of the attraction of the oppositely charged electron and proton, the electron might be expected to revolve in an orbit about the much heavier proton in a way similar to that in which the earth revolves about the sun. Bohr suggested that the orbit of the electron in the normal hydrogen atom should be circular, with radius 0.530 Å. The electron was calculated to be going around this orbit with the constant speed 2.18×10^8 cm/sec, which is a little less than one percent of the speed of light (3×10^{10} cm/sec, about 186,000 miles per second).

As a result of studies made by many physicists, this picture is now known to be nearly but not quite right. The electron does not move in a definite orbit, but rather in a somewhat random way, so that it is sometimes very close to the nucleus and sometimes rather far away. Moreover, it moves mainly toward the nucleus or away from it, and it travels in all directions about the nucleus instead of staying in one plane. Although it does not stay just 0.530 Å from the nucleus, this is its most probable distance. Actually by moving around rapidly it effectively occupies all the space within a radius of about 1 Å of the nucleus, and so gives the hydrogen atom an effective diameter of about 2 Å. It is because of this motion of electrons that atoms, which are made of particles only 0.0001 Å in diameter, act as solid objects several Å in diameter. The speed of the electron in the hydrogen atom is not constant; but its average is the Bohr value 2.18×10^8 cm/sec.

Thus we can describe the free hydrogen atom as having a heavy nucleus at the center of a sphere defined by the space filled by the fast-moving electron in its motion about the nucleus. This sphere is about 2 Å in diameter.

The Electronic Structure of the Noble Gases. Electron Shells.   The distributions of electrons in atoms of the noble gases have been determined by physicists by methods that are too complex to be discussed here. The results obtained are shown in Figure 5-3. It is seen that *the electrons are not uniformly arranged about the atomic nuclei, but are instead arranged in concentric shells.*

The **helium atom** contains two electrons, each of which carries out motion about the helium nucleus similar to that of the one electron in the hydrogen atom. These two electrons are said to occupy the

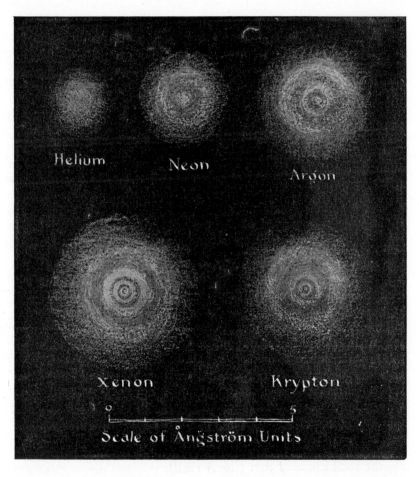

FIGURE 5-3   *Drawing of electron distributions in noble-gas atoms, showing successive electron shells.*

K shell.* This shell, of two electrons only, is the smallest of the concentric shells of electrons that any atom can have. Only two electrons can be put in the K shell. *All of the atoms heavier than hydrogen have two K electrons close to the nucleus.*

The **neon atom** consists of two K electrons close to the nucleus and an **outer shell of eight L electrons.** Thus the neon atom is more complicated than the helium atom, inasmuch as it has two shells instead of one.

The **argon atom** has in addition to the K shell of two electrons and the L shell of eight electrons another shell of eight electrons, the **M shell.**

Both neon and argon are hence built up from the preceding noble gas by increasing the nuclear charge by eight and by adding a new outer shell of eight electrons. This relation does not hold, however, with the noble gases heavier than the first three. **Krypton** has, it is true, a new outer shell of eight electrons, the **N shell,** but also the *next inner shell, the M shell, has* **expanded** *from eight to eighteen electrons.* Thus the electronic structure of krypton is obtained from that of argon by adding eighteen electrons, ten of which enter the shell which is outermost in the argon atom, the remaining eight forming a new outer shell.

At **xenon** there is added a new outer shell of electrons, the **O shell,** and again the next inner shell (the N shell) has expanded from eight to eighteen electrons.

Thus *each of the two short periods in the periodic table involves the addition of a new outer shell of eight electrons; and each of the two long periods involves the addition of a new outer shell of eight electrons and also the insertion of ten electrons into the next inner shell.*

The very long period of the periodic table, which is completed at **radon,** involves the addition of a new outer shell of eight electrons, the

TABLE 5-3   *Electron Shells of the Noble Gases*

ATOM	ATOMIC NUMBER	K	L	M	N	O	P
He	2	2					
Ne	10	2	8				
A	18	2	8	8			
Kr	36	2	8	18	8		
Xe	54	2	8	18	18	8	
Rn	86	2	8	18	32	18	8

P shell, the insertion of ten additional electrons into the next inner shell (the O shell), and also the insertion of fourteen additional electrons into the shell inside of that (the N shell).

* The use of the letter K for the innermost electron shell in an atom, and of $L, M, \cdots$ for other shells, is the result of historic accident. The letters are not abbreviations of words.

These successive shells K, L, M, N, O, P are also represented by the numbers 1, 2, 3, 4, 5, 6, which are the values of the *quantum number* that enters into the treatment of the electrons according to the quantum theory.

The electronic structures of the noble gases are summarized in Table 5-3.

The numbers 2, 8, 18, 32, which are the maximum numbers of electrons which can occupy the successive shells K, L, M, and N, are seen to be equal to $2n^2$, with $n = 1$, 2, 3, and 4, respectively.

Subshells of Electrons.   A given shell may be occupied by any number of electrons up to its maximum capacity. Atoms with 2, 8, 18, and 32 electrons in a shell are, however, especially stable. Thus the N shell contains 8 electrons in krypton, 18 in xenon, and 32 in radon.

The stability of these numbers results from the fact that each shell (except the K shell) consists of two or more subshells. The L shell contains a $2s$ subshell of 2 electrons and a $2p$ subshell of 6 electrons; for the other shells the subshells are as shown in Table 5-4.*

TABLE 5-4   *Subshells of Electrons*

	SUBSHELLS	NUMBER OF ELECTRONS			
K shell:	$1s$	2			
L shell:	$2s$	2	8		
	$2p$	6			
M shell:	$3s$	2	8	18	
	$3p$	6			
	$3d$	10			
N shell:	$4s$	2	8	18	32
	$4p$	6			
	$4d$	10			
	$4f$	14			

The Structure of Other Atoms.   Each of the elements from lithium to neon, in the first short period of the periodic system, has an inner K shell of 2 electrons and an outer L shell containing from one to eight electrons.

The electronic structure of atoms is often represented by *electron–dot symbols*, usually drawn by showing only the electrons of the outer shell. These symbols for the atoms lithium to neon are accordingly the following:

$$\text{Li} \cdot \qquad \text{Be} \cdot \qquad \overset{\cdot}{\text{B}} \cdot \qquad \cdot \overset{\cdot}{\text{C}} \cdot \qquad : \overset{\cdot}{\text{N}} \cdot \qquad : \overset{\cdot}{\underset{\cdot \cdot}{\text{O}}} \cdot \qquad : \overset{\cdot}{\underset{\cdot \cdot}{\text{F}}} \cdot \qquad : \overset{\cdot \cdot}{\underset{\cdot \cdot}{\text{Ne}}} :$$

* The letters s, p, d, f, etc., like the letters K, L, M, etc., were introduced by spectroscopists long ago, and do not have any deep meaning.

There are four *orbitals* (electron orbits) in the L shell, each of which can be unoccupied, or can be occupied by one electron, or be occupied by two electrons.

Two electrons in an orbital constitute an **electron pair.**

Thus carbon is shown with four unpaired electrons in its L shell; it has just one electron for each of the four orbitals. Neon, however, with eight L electrons, can fit them into the four L orbitals only as four electron pairs. The completed noble-gas outer shell of four electron pairs is called an **octet** of electrons. It is to be noted from Table 5-3 that each of the noble gases has such an outer shell.

The atoms in the second short period may be similarly represented:

$$\overset{\displaystyle\cdot}{\text{Na}}\cdot \quad \overset{\displaystyle\cdot}{\text{Mg}}\cdot \quad \overset{\displaystyle\cdot}{\text{Al}}\cdot \quad \cdot\underset{\displaystyle\cdot}{\overset{\displaystyle\cdot}{\text{Si}}}\cdot \quad \cdot\underset{\displaystyle\cdot}{\overset{\displaystyle\cdot}{\text{P}}}\cdot \quad :\underset{\displaystyle\cdot\cdot}{\overset{\displaystyle\cdot}{\text{S}}}\cdot \quad :\overset{\displaystyle\cdot\cdot}{\underset{\displaystyle\cdot\cdot}{\text{Cl}}}\cdot \quad :\overset{\displaystyle\cdot\cdot}{\underset{\displaystyle\cdot\cdot}{\text{A}}}:$$

The outer electrons in the atoms from sodium to argon occupy the M shell. At argon there are four electron pairs in this shell, occupying four orbitals. However, reference to Table 5-3 shows that the shell has the capacity of holding eighteen electrons, and hence that it consists of nine orbitals altogether, only four of which are occupied in argon.

The first few elements following argon in the periodic table have their outer electrons in the N shell:

$$\overset{\displaystyle\cdot}{\text{K}}\cdot \quad \overset{\displaystyle\cdot}{\text{Ca}}\cdot \quad \overset{\displaystyle\cdot}{\underset{\displaystyle\cdot}{\text{Sc}}}\cdot \quad \cdot\overset{\displaystyle\cdot}{\underset{\displaystyle\cdot}{\text{Ti}}}\cdot$$

However, in the succeeding elements of the first long period of the periodic table the additional electrons are introduced into the unoccupied orbitals of the M shell. Since there are five orbitals in this shell in addition to the four which are occupied in argon, it is possible for ten electrons altogether to be introduced in this way. *The ten elements in the middle of the long period corresponding to these ten additional electrons introduced into the M shell are the iron transition elements.*

It is not customary to represent these M electrons, but only the electrons of the N shell in drawing the electronic structures of the nonmetallic elements of the first long period:

$$\cdot\overset{\displaystyle\cdot}{\underset{\displaystyle\cdot}{\text{Ge}}}\cdot \quad :\overset{\displaystyle\cdot}{\underset{\displaystyle\cdot}{\text{As}}}\cdot \quad :\overset{\displaystyle\cdot\cdot}{\underset{\displaystyle\cdot\cdot}{\text{Se}}}\cdot \quad :\overset{\displaystyle\cdot\cdot}{\underset{\displaystyle\cdot\cdot}{\text{Br}}}\cdot \quad :\overset{\displaystyle\cdot\cdot}{\underset{\displaystyle\cdot\cdot}{\text{Kr}}}:$$

There is no accepted way to represent the electronic structures of the elements in the middle of the long period; sometimes all of the electrons in the M shell are indicated and sometimes only a part of them.

The electron-dot formulas for the elements of the second long period are just the same as for the corresponding elements of the first long period:

$$\text{Rb} \cdot \quad \text{Sr} \cdot \quad \text{Y} \cdot \quad \cdot \text{Zr} \cdot$$

and $\cdot \text{Sn} \cdot \quad : \text{Sb} \cdot \quad : \text{Te} \cdot \quad : \overset{..}{\text{I}} \cdot \quad : \overset{..}{\text{Xe}} :$

The very long period begins with the three elements cesium, barium, and lanthanum, the outer electrons of which are in the O shell:

$$\text{Cs} \cdot \quad \text{Ba} \cdot \quad \text{La} \cdot$$

The fourteen elements following lanthanum are the lanthanons. They correspond to the introduction of fourteen additional electrons into the N shell, bringing its total number of electrons up to 32. The remaining elements are similar to those shown directly above them in the periodic table, and their electronic structures are similarly represented.

Illustrative Exercises

5-1.   (a) Without referring to the text, draw electron-dot symbols of atoms of the elements from lithium to neon, showing 1 to 8 electrons of the L shell. (b) What electrons in these atoms are not represented by dots in these symbols?

5-2.   The alkali metals, group I of the periodic table, are Li, Na, K, Rb, Cs, and Fr. Their atomic numbers are 3, 11, 19, 37, 55, and 87, respectively. (a) How do they differ in electronic structure from the noble gases that precede them in the periodic table? (b) Write electron-dot symbols for them.

5-3.   The halogens, group VII of the periodic table, are F, Cl, Br, I, and At, with atomic numbers 9, 17, 35, 53, and 85, respectively. Write electron-dot symbols for them, showing only electrons of the outermost shell.

5–6. Ionization Energies of the Elements

The chemical properties of elements are determined by the number of electrons in their atoms and also by the strength with which the electrons are held.

The helium atom contains two electrons, both of which are held tightly by the attraction of the nucleus. It is possible to remove one of these electrons, if a supply of energy is at hand.

The reaction we are considering is

$$\text{He} \longrightarrow \text{He}^+ + e^-$$

Here He^+ is the symbol for the *helium ion*, consisting of a helium nucleus, with charge $+2e$, and one electron, with charge $-e$; the helium ion thus has the residual charge $+e$ (represented in the symbol by the superscript $+$). The reaction is said to *ionize* the helium atom.

Ions are of great importance in chemistry, and we must now define the word ion:*

---

* The word ion is derived from the Greek word meaning to go, to move.

*An **ion** is an atom or group of atoms that is not electrically neutral, but instead carries a positive or negative electric charge.*

An atom (or group of atoms) is electrically neutral when the number of electrons surrounding the nucleus (or nuclei) is exactly equal to the atomic number (or sum of the atomic numbers). It is a positive ion if one or more electrons are missing, and it is a negative ion if it has one or more extra electrons.

Ionization is the process of producing ions from neutral atoms or molecules, by removing electrons or adding electrons.

The amount of energy required to remove an electron is called the *ionization energy* of the atom. It is customary to give values of this quantity in electron-volts (ev); one electron-volt is equal to 23,053 cal/mole.

The first ionization energy of helium (removing one electron) is 24.48 ev, and the second (removing the second electron) is 54.14 ev. Many values have also been determined by study of the spectra of the atoms.

Ionization energies of the elements from hydrogen to argon are given in Table 5-5, and values of the first ionization energy for the first sixty elements are plotted in Figure 5-4.

It is seen that there is a striking correlation of these values with the periodic table. The ionization-energy curve has sharp maxima at $Z = 2, 10, 18, 36,$ and 54; that is, at the noble gases. These are immediately followed by deep minima, for the soft metals lithium, sodium, potassium, rubidium, and cesium, which were described in Section 5–1 as being closely similar to one another in properties.

We may well feel that the resistance that atoms of the noble gases offer to giving up any of their electrons is closely related to their striking chemical inertness. A further discussion of this question will be given in Chapter 10.

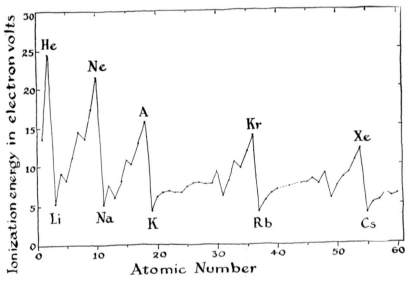

FIGURE 5-4   *The ionization energy, in electron-volts, of the first electron of atoms from hydrogen, atomic number 1, to neodymium, atomic number 60. Symbols of the elements with very high and very low ionization energy are shown in the figure.*

TABLE 5-5

Z	ELEMENT	NUMBERS OF ELECTRONS					IONIZATION ENERGIES, IN ELECTRON-VOLTS			
		1s	2s	2p	3s	3p	1st	2nd	3rd	4th
1	H	1					13.60			
2	He	2					24.58	54.40		
3	Li	2	1				5.39	75.62	122.42	
4	Be	2	2				9.32	18.21	153.85	217.66
5	B	2	2	1			8.30	25.15	37.92	259.30
6	C	2	2	2			11.26	24.38	47.86	64.48
7	N	2	2	3			14.54	29.61	47.43	77.45
8	O	2	2	4			13.61	35.15	54.93	77.39
9	F	2	2	5			17.42	34.98	62.65	87.23
10	Ne	2	2	6			21.56	41.07	64.	97.16
11	Na	2	2	6	1		5.14	47.29	71.65	98.88
12	Mg	2	2	6	2		7.64	15.03	80.12	109.29
13	Al	2	2	6	2	1	5.98	18.82	28.44	119.96
14	Si	2	2	6	2	2	8.15	16.34	33.46	45.13
15	P	2	2	6	2	3	11.0	19.65	30.16	51.35
16	S	2	2	6	2	4	10.36	23.4	35.0	47.29
17	Cl	2	2	6	2	5	13.01	23.80	39.90	53.5
18	A	2	2	6	2	6	15.76	27.62	40.90	59.79

Illustrative Exercises

5-4.   The first ionization energy of helium is 24.58ev, and the second is 54.40ev. In each case a $1s$ electron is removed. Can you explain why the second $1s$ electron is held so much more tightly than the first?

5-5.   What are the electron configurations of Li^+ and Be^+? Why does the second ionization energy have a much larger value for lithium than for beryllium?

5-7. An Energy-Level Diagram

A diagram representing the distribution of all electrons in all atoms is given in Figure 5-5.

Each orbital is represented by a square. The most stable orbital (its electrons being held most tightly by the nucleus) is the $1s$ orbital, at the bottom of the diagram. Energy is required to lift an electron from a stable orbital to a less stable one, above it in the diagram.

The electrons are shown being introduced in sequence: the first and second in the $1s$ orbital, the next two in the $2s$ orbital, the next six in the $2p$ orbitals, and so on. The sequence is indicated by arrows. The symbol and atomic number of each element are shown adjacent to the outermost electron (least tightly held electron) in the neutral atom.

The distribution of electrons among the orbitals is called the *electron configuration* of the atom. It is represented by the symbols of the subshells with the number of electrons in each subshell given above. Thus the electron configuration of helium is $1s^2$, and that of nitrogen is $1s^2\, 2s^2\, 2p^3$.

For the heavier atoms two or more electron configurations may have nearly the same energy, and there is some arbitrariness in the diagram shown in Figure 5-5. The con-

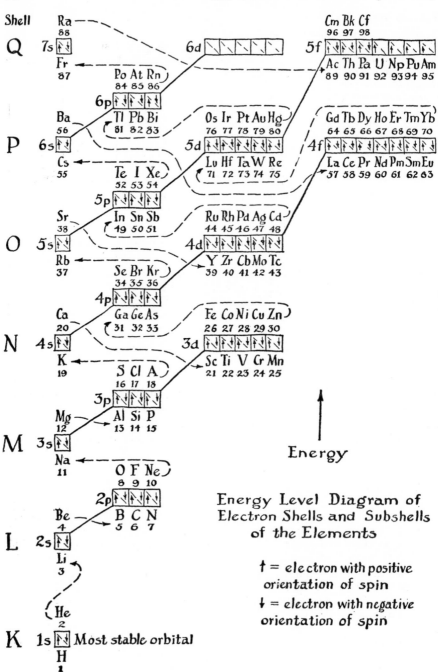

Energy

Energy Level Diagram of
Electron Shells and Subshells
of the Elements

↑ = electron with positive
orientation of spin

↓ = electron with negative
orientation of spin

FIGURE 5-5

figuration shown for each element is either that of the most stable state of the free atom (in a gas) or of a state close to the most stable state.

It was discovered in 1925 that *the electron has a spin*—it rotates about an axis, in the same way that the earth rotates about an axis through its north pole and south pole. An electron can orient its spin in either one of two ways. *Two electrons can occupy the same orbital only if their spins are opposed* (that is, oriented in opposite directions). The spins are represented by arrows in Figure 5-5.

The foregoing italicized sentence is a statement of the **Pauli exclusion principle.** W. Pauli (born 1900) was the first man to notice that an electron excludes another electron with the same orientation of its spin from the orbital it occupies. Hence only two electrons (one pair of electrons) can occupy one orbital, and they must have opposite spins.

Note that it is customary to write electron-dot formulas for some atoms in such a way as to show more unpaired electrons than are indicated in Figure 5-5. For example, in Section 5-5 the electron-dot symbol $\cdot \overset{\cdot}{\underset{\cdot}{C}} \cdot$ was written for carbon. This symbol corresponds to the configuration $1s^2\ 2s\ 2p\ 2p\ 2p$, with four unpaired electrons, whereas in Figure 5-5 it is shown as having the configuration $1s^2\ 2s^2\ 2p\ 2p$, with only two unpaired electrons. The former configuration is the more important one for chemical purposes. You may find it convenient to use electron-dot symbols that differ slightly from those indicated in Figure 5-5.

The Next Chapter. Having discussed the properties and electronic structure of the noble gases, which bear an especially simple relation to the periodic table, we shall now take up the other elements. Hydrogen, the first element, is discussed in the first part of the following chapter. Since we have dealt with helium $(Z = 2)$ in the present chapter, it might be most logical to go on next to lithium $(Z = 3)$ and its congeners. We shall, however, deviate from this order, and take up oxygen $(Z = 8)$ immediately after hydrogen, because of the great importance of the compounds of oxygen.

Illustrative Exercises

5-6. (a) What is the electron configuration of fluorine? (Refer to Figure 5-5, and show all nine electrons. Remember that there are three $2p$ orbitals in the subshell.) (b) How many electron pairs are there in the atom? Which orbitals do they occupy? (c) How many unpaired electrons are there? Which orbital does it occupy?

5-7. (a) What are the electron configurations of beryllium and boron, as shown in Figure 5-5? (b) What electron-dot symbols do they correspond to? (c) What are the customary chemical electron-dot symbols for these atoms? (They show a larger number of unpaired electrons.)

5-8. Can you write the electron configuration for the element with $Z = 102$ (which has not yet been made), showing all 102 electrons? How many electrons are there in each shell (K, L, M, N, O, P, Q)?

Concepts and Terms Introduced in This Chapter

The periodic law; the periodic table.

Successive periods of 2, 8, 8, 18, 18, 32 elements.

Groups of elements; congeners. Metals; metalloids; non-metals.

Noble gases: helium, neon, argon, krypton, xenon, radon.

The electronic structure of the hydrogen atom.

The electronic structure of the noble gases. Electron shells.

Subshells. Orbitals. Electron pairs.

Ions, ionization, ionization energy. The energy-level diagram.

Electron configuration of atoms. The spin of the electron. The Pauli exclusion principle.

Exercises

5-9. Without looking at the periodic table, but by remembering the number of elements in each row (2, 8, 8, 18, 18, 32), deduce what elements have atomic numbers 9, 10, 11, 17, 19, 35, 37, 54.

5-10. Sketch a plan of the periodic table, and fill in from memory the symbols of the first eighteen elements and the remaining alkali metals, halogens, and noble gases.

5-11. By extrapolation with use of the data given in Table 5-2, predict approximate values of the atomic weight, melting point, and boiling point of element 118. What would you expect its chemical properties to be?

5-12. Where was helium first detected? What is the principal source of this element at present?

5-13. List as many uses as you can for the various noble gases.

5-14. What predictions would you make about the formula, color, solubility, taste, and melting point of the compound that would be formed by reaction of chlorine and element 119?

5-15. What are the most important metallic properties? In what part of the periodic table are the elements with metallic properties?

5-16. Classify the following elements as metals, metalloids, or non-metals: potassium, arsenic, aluminum, xenon, bromine, silicon, phosphorus.

Reference Books

Mary Elvira Weeks, *Discovery of the Elements*, Journal of Chemical Education, Easton, Pa. Fourth edition, **1939**.

Many interesting articles about the periodic system of the elements have been published in recent years in the *Journal of Chemical Education*.

Chapter 6

Hydrogen and Oxygen

Hydrogen and oxygen form a great many compounds with other elements, and take part in a great number of chemical reactions. We shall begin our detailed study of descriptive chemistry in this chapter with the study of these two elements, and shall continue, in the following chapter, with another important element, carbon.

Hydrogen, with atomic number 1, is much different in its properties from all of the other elements, and it is therefore not usually classed in a group of the periodic table. Oxygen, with atomic number 8, is the first element of group VI.

Both hydrogen and oxygen are gases at room temperature and atmospheric pressure. It is interesting that it was not until the early years of the seventeenth century that the word "gas" was used. This word was invented by a Belgian physician, J. B. van Helmont (1577–1644), to fill the need caused by the new idea that different kinds of "airs" exist. Van Helmont discovered that a gas (the gas that we now call carbon dioxide) is formed when limestone is treated with acid, and that this gas differs from air in that when respired it does not support life and that it is heavier than air. He also found that the same gas is produced by fermentation, and that it is present in the Grotto del Cane, a cave in Italy in which dogs were observed to become unconscious (carbon dioxide escaping from fissures in the floor displaces the air in the lower part of the cave).

During the seventeenth and eighteenth centuries other gases were discovered, including hydrogen, oxygen, and nitrogen, and many of their properties were investigated. However, it was not until nearly the end of the seventeenth century that these three gases were recognized as elements. When Lavoisier recognized that oxygen is an element, and that combustion is the process of combining with oxygen, the foundation of modern chemistry was laid.

In connection with the discussion of the chemical properties of hydrogen and oxygen in the following sections of this chapter, we shall have occasion to mention some of the principles of chemistry, using the properties of hydrogen and oxygen and their compounds as illustrations. In addition, a discussion will be given in this chapter of chemical nomenclature—the ways in which chemical compounds are named.

6–1. *Hydrogen*

Hydrogen, the first element in the periodic table, is unique: it has no congeners. It is a very widely distributed element. It is found in most of the substances which constitute living matter, and in many inorganic substances. There are more compounds of hydrogen known than of any other element, carbon being a close second. Its most important compound is water, H_2O.

Properties of Hydrogen.   Free hydrogen, H_2, is a colorless, odorless, and tasteless gas. It is the lightest of all gases, its density being about one fourteenth of that of air (Figure 6-1). Its melting point ($-259°$ C or $14°$ A) and boiling point ($-252.7°$ C) are very low, only those of helium being lower. Liquid hydrogen, with density 0.070 g/cm³, is, as might be expected, the lightest of all liquids. Crystalline hydrogen, with density 0.088 g/cm³, is also the lightest of all crystalline substances. Hydrogen is very slightly soluble in water; one liter of water at 0° C dissolves only 21.5 ml of hydrogen gas under 1 atm pressure. The solubility decreases with increasing temperature, and increases with increase in the pressure of the gas.

The Preparation of Hydrogen.   In the laboratory hydrogen may be easily made by the reaction of an acid such as sulfuric acid, H_2SO_4,

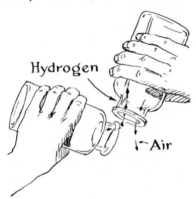

Hydrogen

Air

FIGURE 6-1

Pouring hydrogen from one bottle to another, with downward displacement of air.

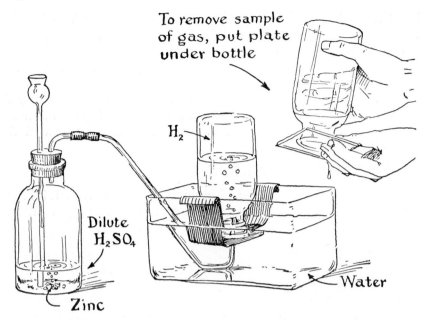

To remove sample
of gas, put plate
under bottle

H_2

Dilute
H_2SO_4

Water

Zinc

FIGURE 6-2   *The preparation of hydrogen in the laboratory.*

with a metal such as zinc. Figure 6-2 represents apparatus used for this purpose. The equation for the reaction is

$$H_2SO_4 + Zn \longrightarrow ZnSO_4 + H_2 \uparrow$$

The vertical arrow placed beside the formula of hydrogen in this equation is used to indicate that hydrogen is a gas, which escapes from the region of reaction.*

Hydrogen can also be prepared by the reaction of some metals with water or steam. Sodium and its congeners react very vigorously with water, so vigorously as to generate enough heat to ignite the liberated hydrogen. An alloy of lead and sodium, which reacts less vigorously, is sometimes used for the preparation of hydrogen. The equation for the reaction of sodium with water is the following:

$$2Na + 2H_2O \longrightarrow 2NaOH + H_2 \uparrow$$

The substance NaOH produced in this way is called *sodium hydroxide*.

Calcium also reacts with water, but with less vigor. The reaction of metallic calcium with cold water provides a simple and safe way of preparing hydrogen in the laboratory. The equation for this reaction is

$$Ca + 2H_2O \longrightarrow Ca(OH)_2 \downarrow + H_2 \uparrow$$

The substance $Ca(OH)_2$ is called *calcium hydroxide*. Calcium hydroxide

* A vertical arrow pointed *down* may be placed after a formula to indicate that the substance precipitates from solution.

is not very soluble in water, and in the course of the reaction of calcium with water a white precipitate of calcium hydroxide is formed.

It is to be seen from the equations above that each of the metals sodium and calcium liberates only half of the hydrogen contained in the water with which it reacts.

Much of the hydrogen that is used in industry is produced by the reaction of iron with steam. The steam from a boiler is passed over iron filings heated to a temperature of about 600° C. The reaction that occurs is

$$3Fe + 4H_2O \longrightarrow Fe_3O_4 + 4H_2$$

After a mass of iron has been used in this way for some time, it is largely converted into iron oxide, Fe_3O_4. The iron can then be regenerated by passing carbon monoxide, CO, over the heated oxide:

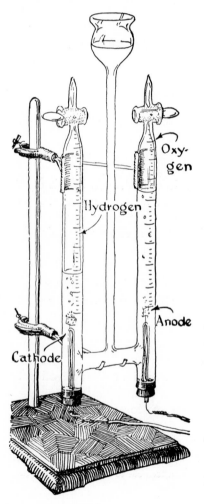

FIGURE 6-3

Apparatus for the electrolysis of water.

$$Fe_3O_4 + 4CO \longrightarrow 3Fe + 4CO_2$$

The carbon monoxide is changed by this reaction into CO_2, carbon dioxide. In this way the iron can be used over and over again.

Hydrogen can also be made by the reaction of a *metallic hydride* (a compound of a metal and hydrogen) with water. Thus calcium hydride, CaH_2, produces hydrogen according to the following reaction:

$$CaH_2 + 2H_2O \longrightarrow Ca(OH)_2 + 2H_2 \uparrow$$

Hydrogen (together with oxygen) can also be made by the *electrolysis* of water. Pure water hardly conducts an electric current at all, but it becomes a good conductor if salt is dissolved in it. When two electrodes are introduced into such a solution and a suitable potential difference of electricity (voltage difference) is applied, hydrogen is liberated at one electrode (the cathode) and oxygen at the other electrode (the anode); this phenomenon of decomposition of a substance by an electric current is called electrolysis. The theory of this phenomenon will be discussed in a later chapter (Chapter 10). The over-all reaction that takes place is represented by the equation

$$2H_2O \longrightarrow 2H_2 \uparrow + O_2 \uparrow$$

Thus two molecules of hydrogen are formed for each molecule of oxygen.

History of the Discovery of Hydrogen.   It was discovered early in the sixteenth century that a combustible gas is formed when sulfuric acid acts upon steel filings or iron nails. Robert Boyle of Oxford observed that hydrogen would not burn in the rarefied atmosphere produced by his air pump. Henry Cavendish in 1781 showed that water is produced when hydrogen combines with oxygen. He did not, however, recognize that the hydrogen had originally been produced from water or acid, but thought that it had come from the metal that reacted with the acid. Cavendish's name for hydrogen was "inflammable air." Lavoisier named the element hydrogen (water-former, from Greek *hydor*, water, and *genon*, to form).

The Uses of Hydrogen in Industry.   Large amounts of hydrogen are used in industry in converting oils (liquid fats), such as cottonseed oil and whale oil, into solid fats, which are used as food or are converted into soap.* Because of its lightness hydrogen may be used to inflate balloons. Hydrogen has a higher conductivity of heat and a lower viscosity than other gases, such as air, and it is for these reasons sometimes used, in a closed system, as a cooling gas around the armatures in large electric generators.

6–2. *Oxygen*

Occurrence of Oxygen.   Oxygen is the most abundant element in the earth's crust. It constitutes by weight 89% of water, 23% of air

* This process is called the *hydrogenation* of oils.

(21% by volume), and nearly 50% of the common minerals (silicates). The average composition of the atmosphere is given in Table 6-1.

TABLE 6-1   *Composition of the Atmosphere*

SUBSTANCE	VOLUME PERCENT IN DRY AIR	SUBSTANCE	VOLUME PERCENT IN DRY AIR
Nitrogen	78.03	Neon	0.0018
Oxygen	20.99	Helium	0.0005
Argon	0.93	Krypton	0.0001
Carbon dioxide	0.03	Ozone	0.00006
Hydrogen	0.01	Xenon	0.000009

The Discovery of Oxygen. Joseph Priestley (1733–1804), of Manchester, England, announced in 1774 the discovery of a gas with the ability to support combustion better than air. He had prepared the gas by heating some red mercuric oxide which was confined in a cylinder over mercury. K. W. Scheele of Sweden seems to have prepared and investigated oxygen before 1773, but an account of his work was not published until 1777.

FIGURE 6-4

The method used by Priestley for preparing oxygen, by heating mercuric oxide with use of a burning glass.

FIGURE 6-5

Apparatus used by Lavoisier to show that when mercury is heated in contact with air one-fifth of the volume of the air combines with the mercury.

FIGURE 6-6 *Lavoisier's apparatus for analyzing water by passing steam over hot iron filings. The undecomposed steam is condensed into water in the cooled coil, and the hydrogen is collected over water in the bell jar.*

Red mercuric oxide, HgO, is made by heating mercuric nitrate, $Hg(NO_3)_2$, which itself is made by the action of nitric acid (HNO_3) on mercury. Priestley found that when mercuric oxide is heated to a high temperature it decomposes with the liberation of oxygen:

$$2HgO \longrightarrow 2Hg + O_2 \uparrow$$

In order to obtain the oxygen he introduced mercuric oxide into the top of a closed tube which had been filled with mercury, its open lower end being under the surface of a bath of mercury. He then heated the mercuric oxide by use of a burning glass (a large glass lens, Figure 6-4), and in this way collected the oxygen over mercury. He found that substances burned in the gas more vigorously than in air.

In 1775 Lavoisier, having learned about Priestley's work, reported his work on the nature of combustion and the oxidation of metals, and advanced his new theory of combustion. He showed that $\frac{1}{5}$ of the volume of air is removed by phosphorus or by mercury (when heated for a long time), and that by strongly heating the mercuric oxide formed in this way a gas with volume equal to the volume lost from the air could be recovered. He showed that this gas supported combustion vigorously, and could, when breathed, support life. The apparatus used by Lavoisier in his work is sketched in Figure 6-5. In 1783 Lavoisier analyzed water by passing steam over hot iron filings (Figure 6-6). Lavoisier named the new gas oxygen (Greek, *oxys*, acid, and *genon*, to form) because he thought, mistakenly, that it was a constituent of all acids.

Preparation and Properties. Ordinary oxygen consists of diatomic molecules, O_2. It is a colorless, odorless gas, which is slightly soluble in water—1 liter of water at $0°$ C dissolves 48.9 ml of oxygen gas at 1 atm pressure. Oxygen condenses to a pale blue liquid at its boiling point, $-183.0°$ C; and on further cooling freezes, at $-218.4°$ C, to a pale blue crystalline solid.

Oxygen may be easily prepared in the laboratory by heating potassium chlorate, $KClO_3$:

$$2KClO_3 \longrightarrow 2KCl + 3O_2 \uparrow$$

The reaction proceeds readily at a temperature just above the melting point of potassium chlorate if a small amount of manganese dioxide, MnO_2, is mixed with it. Although the manganese dioxide accelerates the rate of evolution of oxygen from the potassium chlorate, it itself is not changed.

A substance with this property of accelerating a chemical reaction without itself undergoing significant change is called a **catalyst,** *and is said to* **catalyze** *the reaction.*

Oxygen is made commercially mainly by the distillation of liquid air. Nitrogen is more volatile than oxygen, and tends to evaporate first from liquid air. By properly controlling the conditions of the evaporation nearly pure oxygen can be obtained. The oxygen is stored and shipped in steel cylinders, at pressures of 100 atm or more. Some oxygen is also made commercially, together with hydrogen, by the electrolysis of water.

The Uses of Oxygen. A considerable part of the energy liberated by an ordinary flame is required to heat the nitrogen of the air to the flame temperature, and hence much higher flame temperatures can be reached by using pure oxygen instead of air. An oxygen flame (oxygen and illuminating gas) is used for working glass of high softening point (such as Pyrex glass), and an oxy-hydrogen flame is used for working silica (Figure 6-7). The oxy-acetylene flame (acetylene is a compound of hydrogen and carbon, with formula C_2H_2) and the oxy-hydrogen flame are used for welding iron and steel, and for cutting iron and steel plates as much as several inches thick. The cutting operation is carried out by use of excess of oxygen, which oxidizes some of the iron, and carries it away.

The energy required to keep the human body warm and to carry on the chemical and physical processes involved in life is obtained from chemical reaction of oxygen with organic material derived from or contained in the food which we eat. The oxygen required for this process enters the lungs, is picked up by a protein, hemoglobin, in the red cells of the blood, and is carried by the blood to the tissues, where part of it is released. In case the lungs are damaged by noxious gases or by disease, such as pneumonia, and it becomes difficult for the oxygen of the air to be transferred to the blood at the proper rate, a patient may be aided by being placed in an oxygen-rich atmosphere (40 to 60% oxygen) either in an "oxygen tent" or by use of an oxygen mask. Aviators breathe

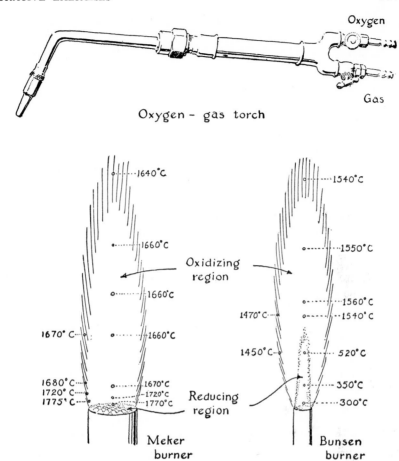

FIGURE 6-7 *Burners and torch.*

pure oxygen at high altitudes, where the pressure of oxygen in the air is insufficient for human needs, and oxygen tanks and helmets are used by rescue workers in gas-filled mines and buildings.

Illustrative Exercises

6-1. Write the chemical equation (balanced, of course) for one reaction that might be used to prepare hydrogen in the laboratory

6-2. Write the equation for a reaction that might be used to prepare oxygen.

6-3. Why is manganese dioxide mixed with potassium chlorate in the usual laboratory procedure for preparing oxygen?

6-4. What is a catalyst?

6-5. (a) Write the equation for the reaction of acetylene, C_2H_2, and oxygen, assuming that the products are water and carbon dioxide, CO_2. (b) Write the equation for the reaction of acetylene and oxygen with products water and carbon monoxide, CO. (c) Under what conditions would you expect the products to be water and carbon dioxide? Water and carbon monoxide?

6–3. *Compounds of Hydrogen and Oxygen.* *The Naming of Chemical Compounds*

Compounds consisting of two elements are called *binary compounds*. For example, water, H_2O, is a binary compound of hydrogen and oxygen, and sodium chloride, NaCl, is a binary compound of sodium and chlorine.

The chemical name of a binary compound is obtained by stating the name of one of the elements, usually the more metallic of the two elements, and adding the name of the second element, with its ending changed to *ide*. The ending ide is characteristic of binary compounds.

Sodium chloride, for example, is a compound of sodium and chlorine. Sodium is a metal, and chlorine is a non-metal. It is accordingly the word chlorine that is modified by the use of the ending ide, so that it become chloride, and this word follows the word sodium in the name sodium chloride.

The symbols for the elements should be written in the same order in the formula, the symbol for the more metallic of the two elements coming first, and that for the less metallic second; for example, NaCl for sodium chloride.

It was mentioned in Chapter 5 that the most strongly metallic elements are those toward the bottom and the left side of the periodic table, and the most strongly non-metallic are those toward the top and the right. Hydrogen is to be considered about equivalent to boron or phosphorus. The chemical name for water is hydrogen oxide; binary compounds of oxygen are called *oxides*.

Sometimes the number of atoms in the formula of a compound is indicated by the use of a prefix. For example, the two oxides, SO_2 and SO_3, of sulfur are called sulfur dioxide and sulfur trioxide, respectively. The prefixes *mono, di, tri, tetra, penta, hexa, hepta,* and *octa* are used to indicate one atom, two atoms, and so on to eight atoms. For example, the molecule N_2O_3 is called dinitrogen trioxide; the prefixes di and tri indicate that the molecule contains two atoms of nitrogen and three atoms of oxygen.

Many metals form two oxides (some of them form more than two). It is customary in the case of metals to make use of a suffix to the name of the metal in order to distinguish between the oxides. The suffix *ous* is used for the compound containing the smaller amount of oxygen (or other non-metallic element), and the suffix *ic* is used for the compound containing the larger amount of oxygen (or other non-metallic element).

Often these suffixes are used with the Latin name of the element, rather than the English name. For example, the metal tin (Latin name *stannum*, symbol Sn) forms two oxides, SnO and SnO_2. These are named stannous oxide and stannic oxide, respectively.

The Compounds of Oxygen.   Oxides of all of the elements have been prepared, except the noble gases. Examples are sodium oxide, Na_2O; magnesium oxide, MgO; aluminum oxide, Al_2O_3; zinc oxide, ZnO; sulfur dioxide, SO_2. Most of the elementary substances combine so vigorously with oxygen that they will burn, either spontaneously (phosphorus) or after they have been ignited, by heating (sulfur, hydrogen, sodium, magnesium, iron, etc.). A few metals, such as copper and mercury, form oxides only slowly, even when heated; in some cases it is necessary to prepare oxides by indirect methods, rather than by direct reaction with oxygen. The properties of oxides are discussed in later sections of the book.

The Compounds of Hydrogen.   Hydrogen forms binary compounds with all of the metalloids and non-metals except the noble gases. It also combines with many of the metals.

The compounds of hydrogen with metals and metalloids are called *hydrides:* an example is lithium hydride, LiH.

Many of the compounds of hydrogen with non-metallic elements have special names; for example, CH_4, methane; NH_3, ammonia; H_2O, water; SiH_4, silane; PH_3, phosphine; and AsH_3, arsine.

Illustrative Exercises

6-6.   Assign names to the following binary compounds: MgO, NaH, KCl, CaH_2, Al_2O_3, SiO_2, CaS, Na_2O, Li_3N, AlF_3.

6-7.   The following pairs of elements form binary compounds in which the atoms of the two elements occur in equal numbers. Write formulas for them, and assign names to them: cesium and fluorine; nitrogen and boron; oxygen and beryllium; carbon and silicon; aluminum and phosphorus; chlorine and fluorine.

6-8.   Using prefixes to indicate the number of atoms of different kind, assign names to the following binary compounds: $MgCl_2$, BF_3, SiO_2, PCl_5, SF_6, CO, CO_2, SO_2, SO_3, $SiCl_4$.

6–4. *Oxidation and Reduction*

Hydrogen combines with oxygen with great vigor. A stream of hydrogen when ignited burns in oxygen or air with a very hot, almost colorless flame (Figure 6-8), and a mixture of hydrogen and oxygen when ignited explodes with great violence.

When hydrogen burns in air or oxygen, forming hydrogen oxide

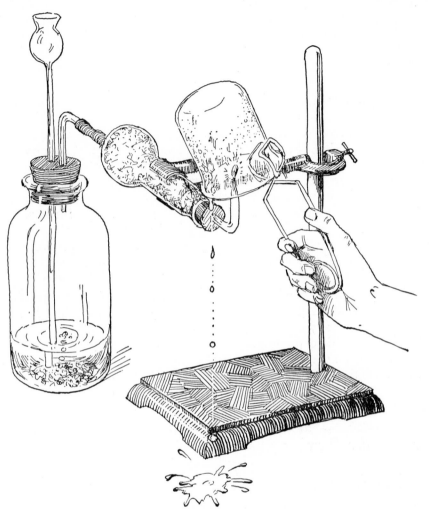

FIGURE 6-8   *The formation of water by burning hydrogen.*

(water), the hydrogen is said to have been *oxidized*. The process is called *oxidation*, and oxygen is called the *oxidizing agent*.

The tendency of hydrogen to combine with oxygen to form water is so great that the gas will even remove oxygen from many metallic oxides. Thus when a stream of hydrogen is passed over hot copper oxide, CuO, in a heated tube, the copper oxide is converted into metallic copper (Figure 6-9):

$$CuO + H_2 \longrightarrow Cu + H_2O$$

This reaction is described as the *reduction* of copper oxide by hydrogen. Hydrogen is called the *reducing agent* in the reaction. Copper oxide is said to have been *reduced* to metallic copper.

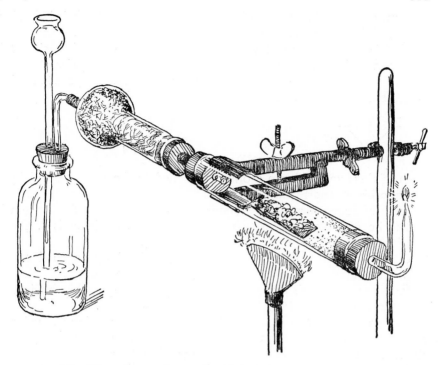

FIGURE 6-9   *The reduction of a metal oxide by hydrogen.*

In the reaction of hydrogen and copper oxide the copper oxide is the oxidizing agent. In every reaction of this sort there is a reducing agent which is oxidized and an oxidizing agent which is reduced.

Illustrative Exercises

6-9.   (a) In the reaction of acetylene and oxygen to form water and carbon dioxide, what is the reducing agent? (b) What is the oxidizing agent? (c) What substance has been oxidized?

6-10.   Write the equation for the reaction of reduction of ferrous oxide, FeO, to iron by use of hydrogen as the reducing agent.

6–5. *Valence*

If there were no order in the way in which atoms of different elements combine to form the molecules and crystals of compounds, it would be necessary for us to memorize one by one the formulas of thousands of substances. Fortunately there is a great deal of order in the formulas of substances, resulting from the fact that some elements have a definite combining capacity, or *valence* (from Latin *valentia*, vigor or capacity), which determines the number of other atoms with which an atom of the element can combine. Other elements, more complex in their behavior, may exhibit any one of two or more combining capacities.

The simplest concept of valence is that *the* **valence** *of an element is the number of bonds that an atom of the element can form with other atoms.*

For example, we may assign to the water molecule, H_2O, the following **valence-bond structure:**

$$
\begin{array}{ccc}
H & & H \\
\diagdown & & \diagup \\
& O &
\end{array}
$$

Each of the two hydrogen atoms is attached to the oxygen atom by a **valence bond,** represented by the line connecting the symbols for the atoms. Hydrogen forms one valence bond: the valence of hydrogen is said to be 1. Oxygen forms two valence bonds; its valence is 2. These are the usual valences of hydrogen and oxygen.

The binary compound of hydrogen and chlorine is hydrogen chloride, HCl. Assuming that the hydrogen atom forms one bond, the valence-bond structure for this molecule is H—Cl. Accordingly, chlorine in this compound has the valence 1.

Sodium hydride has the formula NaH; hence we assign the valence 1 to sodium also. If sodium retains the valence 1 in other compounds, chlorine the valence 1, and oxygen the valence 2, we would predict for sodium chloride the formula Na—Cl, and for sodium oxide the formula Na—O—Na. Compounds with the formulas NaCl and Na_2O are known.

An element with valence 1 is said to be *univalent.* The Latin prefix uni is used rather than the Greek prefix mono, because the word valence has a Latin root. The adjectives *bivalent, tervalent, quadrivalent, quinque-valent, sexivalent, septivalent,* and *octavalent* are used to describe elements with valences from 2 to 8, respectively.*

Sometimes two or three lines are drawn between two atoms in a valence-bond formula. Two lines drawn between two atoms represent a *double bond,* corresponding to the use of two valences for each atom. Three lines are used to represent a *triple bond.*

The formula NH_3 for ammonia shows that nitrogen is tervalent in this compound, and the formula CH_4 for methane shows that carbon is quadrivalent. The valence-bond formulas for these molecules are the following:

$$
\begin{array}{ccccc}
H & & & H & \\
| & & & | & \\
H-N-H & & & H-C-H & \\
& & & | & \\
& & & H &
\end{array}
$$

* Some chemists use the words monovalent, bivalent, trivalent, tetravalent, pentavalent, hexavalent, etc.

For carbon dioxide, CO_2, we write the valence-bond formula $O{=}C{=}O$. The carbon atom exercises its quadrivalence by forming two double bonds (four bonds altogether) with the two oxygen atoms, and each oxygen atom exercises its bivalence by forming one double bond.

Similarly, the molecule hydrogen cyanide, HCN, is assigned the valence-bond formula $H{-}C{\equiv}N$. Here hydrogen is univalent, carbon is quadrivalent (forming one single bond and one triple bond), and nitrogen is tervalent.

It is sometimes useful to think of the atom as having hooks attached to it, the number of hooks being equal to its valence; the molecule is then considered to be built up by fastening a hook from one atom into a hook of another atom.

There is a close relation between the valence of an element and the position of the element in the periodic table. The maximum valence that an element can have is given by its group number in the table. For example, in the second short period, from sodium, in group I, to chlorine, in group VII, the maximum valence increases from 1, for sodium, to 7, for chlorine. Oxides of the elements in the second short period have been found to have the following formulas:

	Na_2O	MgO	Al_2O_3	SiO_2	P_2O_5	SO_3	Cl_2O_7
Valence of element	1	2	3	4	5	6	7

Throughout the following chapters of our book the relation between the valences of elements and their position in the periodic table will be emphasized.

A more detailed discussion of valence will be presented in Chapters 10, 11, and 12.

Illustrative Exercises

6-11. The valence of chlorine in combination with metals is 1. Predict formulas for the chlorides of sodium, magnesium, aluminum, and silicon.

6-12. Titanium forms an oxide with formula TiO_2. What is the valence of titanium? What would you predict as the formula of a binary compound of titanium and chlorine?

6-13. Boron, in group III of the periodic table, has valence 3. What is the formula of the oxide of boron?

6-6. Ions

In Section 5-6 there was given a brief discussion of ions. We shall now return to this important subject, beginning with an account of their discovery.

Two hundred years ago, during the eighteenth century, scientists (they were then called natural philosophers) were making many discoveries about the nature and properties of electricity. An Italian physicist named Beccaria discovered that pure water is a very poor conductor of electricity. In 1771 the British scientist Henry Cavendish reported that he had found that salt dissolved in water causes the electric conductivity to increase very greatly. Many scientists then carried on investigations of the conductance of electricity by salt solutions, and of chemical reactions produced by electricity, but the discovery of the way in which salt solutions carry an electric current was not made for over one hundred years.

In 1884 a young Swedish scientist Svante Arrhenius (1859–1927), then twenty-five years old, published his doctor's dissertation, on measurements of the electric conductivity of salt solutions and his ideas as to their interpretation. These ideas were rather vague, but he later made them more precise, and then published a detailed paper on ionic dissociation in 1887.

The hypothesis made by Arrhenius is that a solution of salt, such as sodium chloride, contains electrically charged particles, which are called ions (Section 5–6). This hypothesis was not accepted at first, but before long chemists found that it explained so many of the facts of chemistry in a simple way that it was accepted, and it is now an important part of chemical theory.

The electron had not yet been discovered when Arrhenius proposed his theory, but we shall discuss the theory in terms of the electronic structure of ions.

Sodium has atomic number 11. The nucleus of a sodium atom has electric charge $+11e$, and the atom is electrically neutral when the nucleus is surrounded by 11 electrons. If an electron were to be removed from the sodium atom, leaving only 10 electrons around the nucleus, the resulting particle would have a positive charge, $+e$. This particle, composed of a sodium nucleus and 10 electrons, is called a *sodium ion*. Similarly, a chlorine atom, with 17 electrons surrounding a nucleus with charge $+17e$, is converted into a *chloride ion*, with negative charge $-e$, by the addition of an eighteenth electron. The transfer of an electron from a sodium atom to a chlorine atom produces a sodium ion, Na^+, and a chloride ion, Cl^-.

Arrhenius assumed that in a solution of sodium chloride in water there are present sodium ions, Na^+, and chloride ions, Cl^-. When electrodes are put into such a solution, the sodium ions are attracted toward the cathode, and move in that direction, and the chloride ions are attracted toward the anode, and move in the direction of the anode. The motion of these ions, in opposite directions, through the solution provides the mechanism of conduction of the current of electricity by the solution.

Positive ions, which are attracted toward the cathode, *are called* **cations.** *Negative ions*, which are attracted toward the anode, *are called* **anions.**

It is now known that a crystal of sodium chloride is also composed of ions, sodium ions, Na^+, and chloride ions, Cl^-, arranged as shown in Figure 4-6; it is not composed of neutral atoms of sodium and chlorine.

6–7. *Acids, Bases, and Salts*

The Nature of Acids and Bases. The alchemists observed that many different substances when dissolved in water give solutions with certain properties in common, such as acidic taste and the property of reacting with metals such as zinc with liberation of hydrogen. These substances were classed as *acids*. It is now known that the acidic properties of the solutions are due to the presence of *hydrogen ion*, H^+, in concentration greater than in pure water.

The usage of the word acid is variable. For many purposes it is convenient to say that an **acid** *is a hydrogen-containing substance which dissociates on solution in water to produce hydrogen ion.*

Examples of acids are

Hydrochloric acid, HCl (hydrogen chloride)
Hydrobromic acid, HBr (hydrogen bromide)
Hydrosulfuric acid, H_2S (hydrogen sulfide)
Sulfuric acid, H_2SO_4
Sulfurous acid, H_2SO_3
Phosphoric acid, H_3PO_4
Nitric acid, HNO_3
Perchloric acid, $HClO_4$
Chloric acid, $HClO_3$
Carbonic acid, H_2CO_3

A **base** *is a substance containing the hydroxide ion, OH^-, or the hydroxide group, OH, which can dissociate in aqueous solution as the hydroxide ion, OH^-.* Basic solutions have a characteristic brackish taste.

Hydroxides of metals are compounds of metals with the hydroxide group, OH. The hydroxides of the metals are bases. The hydroxides LiOH, NaOH, KOH, RbOH, and CsOH are called *alkalies;* and those $Be(OH)_2$, $Mg(OH)_2$, $Ca(OH)_2$, $Sr(OH)_2$, and $Ba(OH)_2$ are called *alkaline earths*. A basic solution is also called an *alkaline solution*.

Acids and bases react to form compounds which are called **salts.** Thus the reaction of sodium hydroxide and hydrochloric acid produces the salt sodium chloride, NaCl, and water:

$$NaOH + HCl \longrightarrow NaCl + H_2O$$

Similarly the reaction of calcium hydroxide and phosphoric acid produces water and calcium phosphate, $Ca_3(PO_4)_2$:

$$3Ca(OH)_2 + 2H_3PO_4 \longrightarrow Ca_3(PO_4)_2 + 6H_2O$$

Hydrogen Ion (Hydronium Ion) and Hydroxide Ion.   The hydrogen ion, H^+, has a very simple structure: it consists of a bare proton, without the electron that is attached to it in a hydrogen atom. The hydrogen ion has a positive electric charge of one unit. The bare proton, H^+, does not exist in appreciable concentration in aqueous solutions, but instead exists attached to a water molecule, forming the *hydronium ion*, H_3O^+.

Because of the additional complexity introduced into chemical equations by use of H_3O^+ in place of H^+, it is customary for the sake of convenience to write equations for reactions of acids in aqueous solution with use of the symbol H^+. It is to be understood that this is a shorthand device, and that the molecular species present is the hydronium ion, H_3O^+.

The hydroxide ion, which is present in basic solutions, carries a negative charge: its formula is OH^-.

Indicators.   Acids and bases have the property of causing many organic substances to change in color. Thus if lemon juice is added to a cup of tea, the tea becomes lighter in color; a dark brown substance in the tea is converted into a light yellow substance. That this change is reversible may be shown by adding an alkaline substance, such as common baking soda (sodium hydrogen carbonate, $NaHCO_3$) to the tea; this will restore the original dark color. A substance that has this property of changing color when acid or base is added to it is called an *indicator*.

A very common indicator is *litmus*, a dye obtained from certain lichens. Litmus assumes a red color in acidic solution and a blue color in basic solution. A useful way of testing the acidity or basicity of a solution is by use of paper in which litmus has been absorbed, called *litmus paper*. A solution which gives litmus paper a color intermediate between blue and red is called a *neutral solution*. Such a solution contains hydrogen ions and hydroxide ions in equal (extremely small) concentrations.

Nomenclature of Acids, Bases, and Salts.   Acids with 1, 2, and 3 replaceable hydrogen atoms are called *monoprotic*, *diprotic*, and *triprotic acids*, respectively, and bases with 1, 2, and 3 replaceable hydroxide groups are called *monohydroxic*, *dihydroxic*, and *trihydroxic bases*. For example, HCl is a monoprotic acid, H_2SO_4 a diprotic acid, and H_3PO_4 a triprotic acid. NaOH is a monohydroxic base, and $Ca(OH)_2$ a dihydroxic base.

Salts such as Na_2SO_4, which result from complete neutralization of an acid by a base, are called *normal salts;* those containing more acid are called *acid salts*.

The ways of naming salts are illustrated by the following examples; older names which are now not approved are given in parentheses:

Na_2SO_4:   sodium sulfate, normal sodium sulfate

$NaHSO_4$:   sodium hydrogen sulfate; sodium acid sulfate; (sodium bisulfate)

Na_3PO_4:   normal sodium phosphate; trisodium phosphate

Na_2HPO_4:   disodium monohydrogen phosphate; sodium mono-hydrogen phosphate

NaH_2PO_4:   sodium dihydrogen phosphate

There are three kinds of names given in the list of acids at the beginning of this section. A name of one kind, illustrated by hydrochloric acid, has the prefix *hydro* and the suffix *ic* attached to the name of the element characteristic of the acid. The molecules of acids with names of this kind do not contain oxygen. The salts are named by omitting the prefix *hydro*, and replacing the suffix *ic* by the suffix *ide*. Thus the sodium salt of hydrochloric acid is sodium chloride.

The names of some other acids, such as sulfuric acid, have the same suffix, *ic*, but no prefix. The molecules of these acids contain oxygen atoms. The salts are named simply by changing the suffix to *ate*. Thus the normal sodium salt of sulfuric acid is sodium sulfate.

Sulfurous acid is a representative of another class of acids, the names of which have the suffix *ous*. In general these acids have fewer oxygen atoms in the molecule than the corresponding *ic* acids. The salts are named by changing the suffix *ous* to *ite*. Thus the normal sodium salt of sulfurous acid is sodium sulfite.

A few acids have names that do not fit into this classification, but they are not very important.

Acidic Oxides and Basic Oxides.   An oxide such as sulfur trioxide, SO_3, or diphosphorus pentoxide, P_2O_5, which does not contain hydrogen but which with water forms an acid, is called an *acidic oxide* or *acid anhydride*. The equations for the reactions of formation of the corresponding acids from these oxides are the following:

$$SO_3 + H_2O \longrightarrow H_2SO_4$$

$$P_2O_5 + 3H_2O \longrightarrow 2H_3PO_4$$

The oxides of most of the non-metallic elements are acidic oxides.

An oxide which with water forms a base is called a *basic oxide*. The oxides of the metals are basic oxides (even though some of them are very little affected by water). Thus sodium oxide, Na_2O, reacts with water to form a base, sodium hydroxide:

$$Na_2O + H_2O \longrightarrow 2NaOH$$

Acidic oxides and basic oxides may combine directly with one another to form salts:

$$Na_2O + SO_3 \longrightarrow Na_2SO_4$$
$$3CaO + P_2O_5 \longrightarrow Ca_3(PO_4)_2$$

Illustrative Exercises

6-14. Write the equation for the reaction of sodium hydroxide and perchloric acid, to form sodium perchlorate.

6-15. Write equations for three reactions of potassium hydroxide and phosphoric acid, to form three potassium salts of phosphoric acid, representing replacement of 1, 2, and 3 atoms of hydrogen by atoms of potassium. Write names for the three salts.

6-16. What is the formula of normal calcium sulfide?

6-17. Nitrous acid has the formula HNO_2. Write an equation for the reaction of formation of its sodium salt. What is the name of this salt?

6-18. Dichlorine heptoxide, Cl_2O_7, is the anhydride of perchloric acid. Write the equation for the reaction of the heptoxide with water to form the acid.

6-19. What is the anhydride of carbonic acid, H_2CO_3?

6–8. The Ionization of Acids, Bases, and Salts

Most salts, like sodium chloride, dissolve in water to form solutions with large electric conductivity. The conductivity of the solutions is so large as to show that the *salts are completely ionized* in aqueous solution.

For example, the substance sodium sulfate, Na_2SO_4, dissolves in water to form a solution containing sodium ions, Na^+, and sulfate ions, SO_4^{--}. An ion such as the sulfate ion, a group of two or more atoms with an electric charge, is called a *complex ion*.

Some acids and bases are also completely ionized in aqueous solution. For example, hydrochloric acid, a solution of hydrogen chloride, HCl, in water, contains hydrogen ion, H^+, and chloride ion, Cl^-, and only a few undissociated hydrogen chloride molecules, HCl. Similarly, a solution of sodium hydroxide, $NaOH$, contains the sodium ion, Na^+, and the hydroxide ion, OH^-.

Some acids and bases, and also a few salts, are, however, only partially ionized in solution. For example, acetic acid when dissolved in water produces a solution containing rather small amounts of hydrogen ion, H^+, and acetate ion, $C_2H_3O_2^-$, and a large amount of undissociated molecules of acetic acid, $HC_2H_3O_2$. The acids and bases that are completely ionized in aqueous solution are called *strong acids* and *strong bases*. Those that are only partially ionized are called *weak acids* and *weak bases*.

An example of a salt that is only partially ionized in aqueous solution

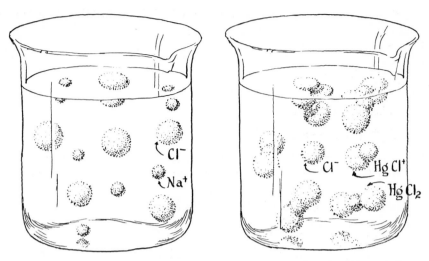

FIGURE 6-10   *A solution of a completely dissociated salt (at the left) and of a partially dissociated salt (at the right).*

is mercuric chloride, $HgCl_2$. A solution of mercuric chloride contains the molecular species* $HgCl_2$, $HgCl^+$, Hg^{++}, and Cl^-, all in appreciable concentrations. This substance is exceptional—most salts are completely ionized.

Acids, bases, and salts that are completely ionized are called *strong electrolytes;* those that are only partially ionized are called *weak electrolytes.* The difference between a solution of a strong electrolyte and a solution of a weak electrolyte is illustrated in Figure 6-10.

Writing Equations for Ionic Reactions.   In writing an equation for a chemical reaction between strong electrolytes in solution, *ions* should usually be written as reactants and products.† Thus the precipitation of silver chloride on the addition of a solution of hydrochloric acid to a solution of silver nitrate should be written

$$Ag^+ + Cl^- \longrightarrow AgCl \downarrow$$

and not

$$AgNO_3 + HCl \longrightarrow AgCl \downarrow + HNO_3$$

Silver nitrate, hydrochloric acid, and nitric acid are all strong electrolytes, and their solutions consist nearly entirely of the dissociated ions. The ionic equation written above accordingly represents the actual

---

* It is customary to use the term "molecular species" to refer to ions as well as neutral molecules.

† Sometimes the use of molecular formulas in equations is advantageous, in that it shows what reagents are to be used in an experiment.

reaction that takes place in the beaker, which is simply the combination of silver ion and chloride ion to form the product, silver chloride. It is true that nitrate ion was present in solution with the silver ion, and that hydrogen ion was present with the chloride ion; but these ions remain in essentially their original state after the reaction has occurred, and there is hence usually no reason to indicate them in the equation.

The same equation

$$Ag^+ + Cl^- \longrightarrow AgCl \downarrow$$

is, moreover, applicable also to the precipitation of, say, silver perchlorate solution (containing Ag^+ and ClO_4^-) by sodium chloride solution (containing Na^+ and Cl^-).

A good rule to follow is *to write the chemical equation to correspond as closely as possible to the actual reaction, showing the molecules or ions which actually react and are formed.*

In accordance with this rule, either the ions or the molecules might be shown for reactions involving weak electrolytes. If a substance is not ionized at all, the formula for its molecules should be used in the equation.

Illustrative Exercises

6-20. (a) Hydrochloric acid, HCl, is a strong acid. What molecular species are present in a dilute aqueous solution of this acid? (b) Sodium hydroxide, NaOH, is a strong base. What molecular species are present in its solution? (c) Write an equation for the reaction that occurs when these two solutions are mixed.

6-21. When a solution of silver nitrate, containing the ions Ag^+ and NO_3^- (nitrate ion), is added to a solution of sodium chloride a white precipitate of the insoluble substance silver chloride, AgCl, is formed. (a) Write the equation for this reaction. (b) What molecular species remain in the solution?

6–9. *Ozone. The Phenomenon of Allotropy*

Ozone is a blue gas which has a characteristic odor (its name is from the Greek *ozein*, to smell) and is a stronger oxidizing agent than ordinary oxygen. It is formed when an electric current is passed through oxygen (Figure 6-11).

Although its properties are different from those of ordinary oxygen, ozone is not a compound, but is elementary oxygen in a different form— a form with three atoms in the molecule (O_3) instead of two, as in ordinary oxygen (Figure 6-12).

The existence of an elementary substance in two or more forms is called **allotropy** (Greek *allotropia*, variety, from *allos*, other, and *tropos*, direction). Ordinary oxygen and ozone are the **allotropes** of oxygen. Allotropy is shown by many elements; it is due either to the existence of two of more kinds of molecules (containing different numbers of atoms) or to the

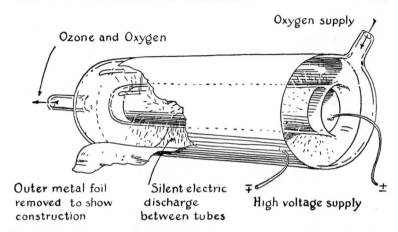

Ozone and Oxygen

Oxygen supply

Outer metal foil
removed to show
construction

Silent electric
discharge
between tubes

High voltage supply

FIGURE 6-11   *An ozonizer, for converting oxygen to ozone by use of a silent electric discharge.*

existence of two or more different crystalline forms; that is, of different arrangements of the atoms or molecules in a crystalline array.

Ozone contains more energy than oxygen: the heat evolved when 48 g of ozone* decomposes to oxygen is 32,400 cal, and that amount of energy must have been given to the ozone molecule by the electric discharge when the ozone was formed. Because of its greater energy content, ozone is more reactive than oxygen. It converts mercury and silver into oxides, and it readily frees iodine from potassium iodide, whereas oxygen does not cause these reactions at room temperature.

The Uses of Ozone.   Like some other oxidizing agents (such as chlorine), ozone has the power of converting many colored organic sub-

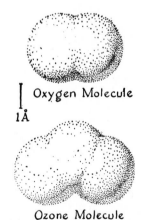

Oxygen Molecule

1 Å

FIGURE 6-12

Molecules of oxygen and ozone. This drawing, like most of the drawings of atoms and molecules in this book, is made with linear magnification about 60,000,000.

Ozone Molecule

* Note the convention in chemistry that "48 g of ozone" is singular in number; it means a quantity of ozone weighing 48 g, rather than forty-eight separate grams of ozone.

stances to colorless products; it accordingly finds use as a bleaching agent for oils, waxes, starch, and flour. It is also used instead of chlorine to sterilize drinking water, by destroying the bacteria in it.

Concepts, Facts, and Terms Introduced in This Chapter

Hydrogen, its physical properties, preparation, uses.

Oxygen, its occurrence, physical properties, preparation, uses.

Potassium chlorate as a source of oxygen; manganese dioxide, a catalyst.

The naming of chemical compounds. Oxides. Hydrides. Oxidation and reduction. Oxidizing agent. Reducing agent.

Valence. Valence bond. Double bond. Triple bond.

Ions. Arrhenius theory of ionization. Cation. Anion. Transfer of electrons between atoms.

Acid. Base. Salt. Hydrogen ion (hydronium ion). Hydroxide ion. Hydroxides of metals. Alkali. Alkaline earth. Indicator. Litmus paper. Nomenclature of acids, bases, and salts. Acidic oxide. Basic oxide.

Writing equations for ionic reactions.

Ozone. Allotropy.

Exercises

6-22. What are allotropes? What differences in properties and structure between oxygen and ozone can you mention?

6-23. Do you know any elements other than oxygen that exist in allotropic forms?

6-24. What is the lightest gas? The lightest liquid? The lightest crystalline substance?

6-25. Write an equation for the preparation of hydrogen by reaction of zinc and hydrochloric acid. (Hydrochloric acid is not so good as sulfuric acid for this preparation, because the hydrogen that is produced is apt to be impure, containing some hydrogen chloride.)

6-26. Write the equation for the neutralization of acetic acid, $HC_2H_3O_2$, by sodium hydroxide. Write the equation for the neutralization of this acid by calcium hydroxide.

6-27. Write an equation for the combustion of phosphorus in oxygen to produce diphosphorus pentoxide, P_2O_5.

6-28. Write equations to represent the formation from sodium hydroxide and phosphoric acid of normal sodium phosphate, disodium monohydrogen phosphate, and sodium dihydrogen phosphate.

6-29. What relative amounts of sodium hydroxide would be required for the three reactions of Exercise 6-28, with the same amount of phosphoric acid?

6-30. What are the acid anhydrides of nitric acid, sulfuric acid, and phosphoric acid? Write the equation for the reaction of the anhydride of nitric acid with water to form the acid.

6-31. When sulfur is burned in air it forms the gas sulfur dioxide, SO_2. What is the formula of the acid of which this gas is the anhydride?

6-32. What uses of ozone are based upon its oxidizing power?

6-33. Assign chemical names to the following compounds: CaH_2, $Ca(OH)_2$, $Mg_3(PO_4)_2$, Li_3N, HI, $KHSO_4$. Which of them are binary compounds?

6-34. Why is the production of hydrogen from iron and steam commercially practical? Write the equation for the reaction.

6-35. What property of hydrogen makes it less desirable than helium for inflating balloons and dirigibles?

6-36. Write the equation for the reaction of citric acid, $H_3C_6H_5O_7$ (the acid present in citrus fruits), and potassium hydroxide to form water and potassium citrate, $K_3C_6H_5O_7$. Is citric acid a monoprotic acid, a diprotic acid, or a triprotic acid?

6-37. Write equations for the neutralization of ammonium hydroxide, NH_4OH, with hydrochloric acid, sulfuric acid, and nitric acid.

Chapter 7

Carbon and Compounds of Carbon

Carbon is the first element of the fourth group of the periodic table, the others being silicon, germanium, tin, and lead (Chapter 26). Carbon forms a great many compounds, and its chemistry is especially interesting to us because most of the substances that make up a human body (and other living organisms) are compounds of carbon. Moreover, the compounds of carbon illustrate well the principles that have been discussed in the preceding chapters and others that need to be discussed. It is for these reasons that we now consider the chemistry of carbon.

Organic Chemistry and Biochemistry. The name *organic chemistry*, which was originally used to refer to the chemistry of substances that occur in living organisms (plants and animals), is now used for *the chemistry of the compounds of carbon*. The chemistry of the elements other than carbon is called *inorganic chemistry*.

Biochemistry may be considered to be a part of organic chemistry. It deals especially with the chemical reactions that take place in living organisms. The manufacture of the artificial fiber nylon, for example, is included in organic chemistry, but not in biochemistry; the structure, methods of synthesis, and general chemical properties of vitamin B_1 are a part of organic chemistry, and the special reactions of this substance in plants and animals are a part of biochemistry.

We shall consider some aspects of organic chemistry and biochemistry throughout this book, beginning in the following paragraphs. A more detailed discussion of organic chemistry will then be given in Chapter 30, and of biochemistry in Chapter 31.

7–1. *Structural Formulas of Carbon Compounds*

The chemistry of carbon was greatly advanced about a century ago through the development of a general *structure theory*, which we shall now discuss in order that the later sections of this chapter may be based on it. This theory is a chemical theory, induced from chemical facts. In recent years it has received added verification through the determination of exact structures of molecules and crystals by physical methods, especially x-ray diffraction, electron diffraction, and the analysis of the spectra of substances.

During the first half of the nineteenth century many organic compounds were obtained from plants and animals or were made in the laboratory. They were analyzed for their constituent elements, and their properties were carefully studied. Efforts were made to find some correlation between the chemical composition and the properties of the substances. These efforts led to the development of the concept of valence and the assignment of valence-bond structures to substances (Section 6–6).

In 1852 the statement was made by E. Frankland, in England, that atoms have a definite combining power, which determines the formulas of compounds. A few years later (1858) a Scottish chemist, Archibald S. Couper, introduced the idea of the valence bond, and drew the first structural formulas. During the same year August Kekulé in Germany showed that carbon is quadrivalent (can form four valence bonds) and that many compounds of carbon involve bonds between carbon atoms.

The structural formula of a carbon compound usually can easily be assigned from a knowledge of the composition of the compound and of some of its properties. Usually each carbon atom forms four valence bonds, each hydrogen atom one, each oxygen atom two, and each nitrogen atom three. (There are some exceptional compounds, which will be discussed later.)

For example, as was mentioned in Section 6–6, methane has the structure

$$H-\overset{\displaystyle H}{\underset{\displaystyle H}{\overset{|}{\underset{|}{C}}}}-H,$$

involving four single bonds, and carbon dioxide has the structure $O{=}C{=}O$, involving two double bonds. A more complex molecule is ethyl alcohol, with the structural formula

$$H-\overset{\displaystyle H}{\underset{\displaystyle H}{\overset{|}{\underset{|}{C}}}}-\overset{\displaystyle H}{\underset{\displaystyle H}{\overset{|}{\underset{|}{C}}}}-O-H.$$

The quadrivalence of the carbon atom is closely related to its electronic structure. The carbon atom has six electrons, two of which, in the K shell (Section 5–5), are very tightly held by the nucleus. The other four, in the L shell, are responsible for the four valence bonds that the carbon atom can form. The electronic structure of the valence bond will be discussed in Chapter 11.

We do not need to know the electronic structure of the valence bond in order to use the chemical structure theory. Indeed, the quadrivalence of carbon was known and structural formulas (valence-bond formulas) of compounds were written by chemists for forty years before the electron was discovered, and another thirty years had gone by before a clear picture had been obtained of the electronic structure of the valence bond. The development, a century ago, of the chemical structure theory as a correlating theory for the mass of information about the chemical properties of substances is one of the greatest of all feats of the human intellect.

7–2. *Elementary Carbon*

Carbon occurs in nature in its elementary state in two allotropic forms: **diamond,** the hardest substance known, which often forms beautiful transparent and highly refractive crystals, used as gems (Figure 7-1); and **graphite,** a soft, black crystalline substance, used as a lubricant and in the "lead" of lead pencils. *Bort* and *black diamond* are imperfectly crystalline forms of diamond, which do not show the cleavage characteristic of diamond crystals. Their density is slightly less than that of crystalline diamond, and they are tougher and somewhat harder. They are used in diamond drills and other grinding devices.

Charcoal, coke, and carbon black (lampblack) are microcrystalline or amorphous (non-crystalline) forms of carbon. The density of diamond is 3.51 g/cm³ and that of graphite is 2.26 g/cm³.

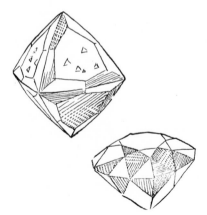

FIGURE 7-1

A natural crystal of diamond, with octahedral faces and smaller faces rounding the edges, and a brilliant-cut diamond.

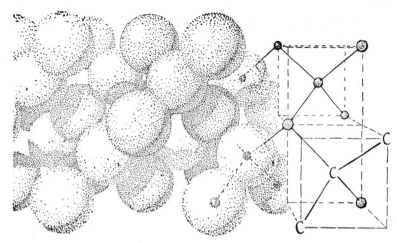

FIGURE 7-2   *The structure of diamond.*

The great hardness of diamond is explained by the structure of the diamond crystal, as determined by the x-ray diffraction method. In the diamond crystal (Figure 7-2) each carbon atom is surrounded by four other carbon atoms, which lie at the corners of a regular tetrahedron about it. A structural formula can be written for a small part of a diamond crystal:

Valence bonds connect each carbon atom with four others. Each of these four is bonded to three others (plus the original one), and so on throughout the crystal. The entire crystal is a giant molecule, held together by valence bonds. To break the crystal many of these valence bonds must be broken; this requires a large amount of energy, and hence the substance is very hard.

The structure of graphite is shown in Figure 7-3. It is a layer structure. Each atom forms two single bonds and one double bond with its three nearest neighbors, as shown in the lowest part of the drawing. The distance between layers is over twice the bond length in a layer (the distance between two bonded atoms). The crystal of graphite can be described as built of giant flat molecules, which are loosely held together in a pile. The layers can be easily separated; hence graphite is a soft substance, which is even used as a lubricant.

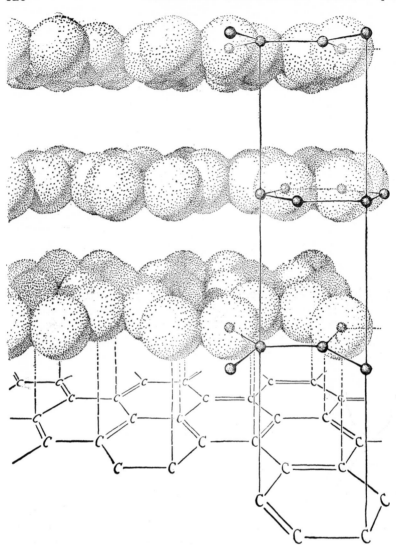

FIGURE 7-3   *The structure of graphite.*

Hardness. The property of hardness is not a simple one to define. It has probably evaded precise definition because the concept of hardness represents a composite of several properties (tensile strength, resistance to cleavage, etc.). Various scales of hardness and instruments for testing hardness have been proposed. One test consists of dropping a diamond-tipped weight on the specimen and measuring the height of rebound. In another test (the Brinell test) a hardened steel ball is pressed into the surface of the specimen, and the size of the produced indentation is measured.

A very simple test of hardness is the scratch test—a specimen that scratches another specimen and is not scratched by it is said to be harder than the second specimen. The scratch-test used by mineralogists is the *Mohs scale*, with reference points (the *Mohs hardness*) from 1 to 10, defined by the following ten minerals:

1. Talc, $Mg_3Si_4O_{10}(OH)_2$
2. Gypsum, $CaSO_4 \cdot 2H_2O$
3. Calcite, $CaCO_3$
4. Fluorite, CaF_2
5. Apatite, $Ca_5(PO_4)_3F$
6. Orthoclase, $KAlSi_3O_8$
7. Quartz, SiO_2
8. Topaz, $Al_2SiO_4F_2$
9. Corundum, Al_2O_3
10. Diamond, C

Diamond is indeed far harder than corundum, and recent modifications of the Mohs scale have been suggested which assign a much larger hardness number, such as 15, to diamond. The hardness of graphite is between 1 and 2.

7–3. *Carbon Monoxide and Carbon Dioxide*

Carbon burns to form the gases *carbon monoxide*, CO, and *carbon dioxide*, CO_2, the former being produced when there is a deficiency of oxygen or the flame temperature is very high.

Carbon Monoxide. Carbon monoxide is a colorless, odorless gas* with small solubility in water (35.4 ml per liter of water at 0° C and 1 atm). It is poisonous, because of its ability to combine with the hemoglobin in the blood in the same way that oxygen does, and thus to prevent the hemoglobin from combining with oxygen in the lungs and carrying it to the tissues. It causes death when about one-third of the hemoglobin in the blood has been converted into carbonmonoxyhemoglobin. The exhaust gas from automobile engines contains some carbon monoxide, and it is accordingly dangerous to be in a closed garage with an automobile whose engine is running. Carbon monoxide is a valuable industrial gas, for use as a fuel and as a reducing agent.

Carbon Dioxide. Carbon dioxide is a colorless, odorless gas with a weakly acid taste, due to the formation of some carbonic acid when it is dissolved in water. It is about 50% heavier than air. It is easily soluble in water, one liter of water at 0° C dissolving 1713 ml of the gas under 1 atm pressure. Its melting point (freezing point) is higher than the point of vaporization at 1 atm of the crystalline form. When crystalline carbon dioxide is heated from a very low temperature, its vapor pressure reaches 1 atm at −79°, at which temperature it vaporizes without melting. If the pressure is increased to 5.2 atm the crystalline substance melts to a liquid at −56.6°. Under ordinary pressure, then, the solid substance is changed directly to a gas. This property has made solid carbon dioxide (Dry Ice) popular as a refrigerating agent.

Carbon dioxide combines with water to form *carbonic acid*, H_2CO_3, a weak acid whose salts are the *carbonates*. The carbonates are important minerals (see calcium carbonate, Section 7–5).

* Until recently chemists were uncertain as to the structural formula of carbon monoxide. It will be described in Chapter 11.

Uses of Carbon Dioxide.   Carbon dioxide is used for the manufacture of *sodium carbonate*, $Na_2CO_3 \cdot 10H_2O$ (washing soda); *sodium hydrogen carbonate*, $NaHCO_3$ (baking soda), and *carbonated water*, for use as a beverage (soda water). Carbonated water is charged with carbon dioxide under a pressure of 3 or 4 atm.

Carbon dioxide can be used to extinguish fires by smothering them. One form of portable fire extinguisher is a cylinder of liquid carbon dioxide—the gas can be liquefied at ordinary temperatures under pressures of about 70 atm. Some commercial carbon dioxide (mainly

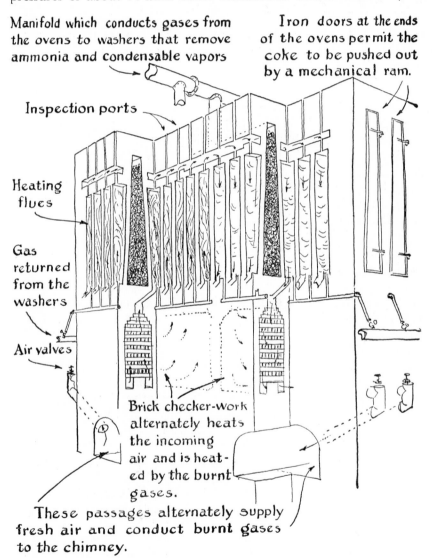

Manifold which conducts gases from the ovens to washers that remove ammonia and condensable vapors

Iron doors at the ends of the ovens permit the coke to be pushed out by a mechanical ram.

Inspection ports

Heating flues

Gas returned from the washers

Air valves

Brick checker-work alternately heats the incoming air and is heated by the burnt gases.

These passages alternately supply fresh air and conduct burnt gases to the chimney.

FIGURE 7-4   *A by-product coke oven.*

solid carbon dioxide) is made from the gas emitted in nearly pure state from gas wells in the western United States. Most of the carbon dioxide used commercially is a by-product of cement mills, lime-kilns, iron blast furnaces, and breweries.

7–4. *Fuels*

Carbon and hydrogen are the principal constituents of the solid fuels coal and wood. Coal has been formed in nature by the slow decomposition of vegetable matter, in the presence of water and absence of air. Most of it was formed during the Carboniferous Period of geologic time, about 250 million years ago (the method of measuring geologic times by use of radioactivity is described in Section 32–2). Coal consists of free carbon mixed with various carbon compounds and some mineral matter. *Anthracite coal* (hard coal) contains only a small amount of volatile matter, and burns with a nearly colorless flame; *bituminous coal* (soft coal) contains much volatile matter, and burns with a smoky flame.

Bituminous coal can be converted into *coke* by heating without access of air. When the heating is carried out in a by-product coke oven, such as that illustrated in Figure 7-4, many substances distill out, including gas for fuel, ammonia, and a complex mixture of liquid and solid organic compounds. The solid material remaining in the ovens, consisting mainly of carbon, is called coke. It burns with a nearly colorless flame, and is used in great amounts in metallurgical processes.

Petroleum is a very important liquid fuel. It is a complex mixture of compounds of carbon and hydrogen.

The gas obtained from a coke furnace (*coal gas*) consists of hydrogen (about 50%), methane, CH_4 (30%), carbon monoxide (10%), and minor components. This coal gas was the original illuminating gas.

Natural gas, from gas wells and oil wells, consists largely of methane.

Producer gas is made by passing a limited supply of air through hot coal or coke (Figure 7-5). The layer of coal or coke which first comes into contact with the stream of air is oxidized to carbon dioxide:

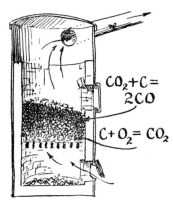

$$CO_2 + C = 2CO$$

$$C + O_2 = CO_2$$

FIGURE 7-5

A furnace for making producer gas.

$$C + O_2 \longrightarrow CO_2$$

As the carbon dioxide rises through the incandescent coke it is reduced to carbon monoxide, which, mixed with nitrogen of the air, escapes from the furnace:

$$CO_2 + C \longrightarrow 2CO$$

Producer gas contains about 25% of carbon monoxide by volume, the rest being nitrogen. Its fuel value is low.

Water gas is made by passing steam through incandescent coke:

$$C + H_2O \longrightarrow CO + H_2$$

This reaction absorbs heat, so that the coke becomes cool. An air blast is then substituted for the steam, until the fuel is heated to a temperature at which it is bright red, and then steam is blown in again. Sometimes a mixture of steam and air is used, instead of alternating the two gases. Water gas and producer gas are used in industrial processes and for domestic heating.

Illustrative Exercises

7-1. Write equations for the reaction of carbon with oxygen when there is a deficiency of oxygen and when there is an excess of oxygen, and for the reaction of carbon monoxide with oxygen. (The blue lambent flame seen over a charcoal fire is due to combustion of carbon monoxide.)

7-2. (a) What is the principal combustible substance in each of the following fuels: coal, coke, coal gas, natural gas, producer gas, water gas? (b) Write the equation for the burning of each of these substances.

7–5. *Carbonic Acid and Carbonates*

When carbon dioxide dissolves in water some of it reacts to form carbonic acid:

$$CO_2 + H_2O \longrightarrow H_2CO_3$$

The structural formula of carbonic acid is $O{=}C\begin{smallmatrix}\nearrow O-H \\ \searrow O-H\end{smallmatrix}$. The acid is diprotic; with a base such as sodium hydroxide it may form both a normal salt, Na_2CO_3, and an acid salt, $NaHCO_3$. The normal salt contains the carbonate ion, CO_3^{--}, and the acid salt contains the hydrogen carbonate ion, HCO_3^-

For many years chemists assigned the structural formula $O{=}C\begin{smallmatrix}\nearrow O^- \\ \searrow O^-\end{smallmatrix}$

to the carbonate ion. With this formula, one of the oxygen atoms is attached to the carbon atom by a double bond, and the other two are attached by single bonds. Then in 1914 W. L. Bragg carried out an x-ray diffraction study of calcite, $CaCO_3$, and found that the three bonds from the carbon atom to the three oxygen atoms in the carbonate ion in this crystal are identical. This new experimental fact required a change in the structural formula. The new structural formula was proposed in 1931, when the chemical *resonance theory* was developed. According to this theory a molecule may have a structure that is a

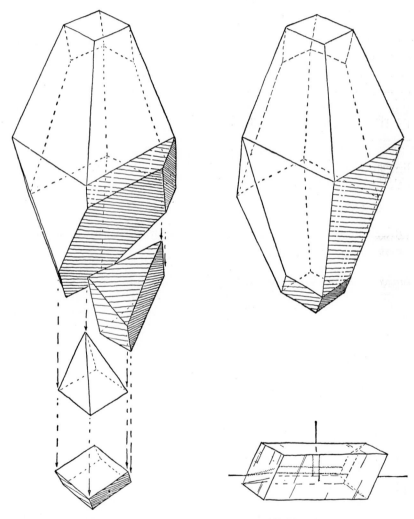

FIGURE 7-6   *Natural crystals of calcite, $CaCO_3$, showing planes of cleavage and how they produce the cleavage rhombohedron (left). The property of birefringence (double refraction) is possessed by calcite (lower right).*

hybrid of two or more valence-bond structures. For the carbonate ion the structure is a hybrid of three structures:

$$\left\{ \begin{matrix} O = C \diagup^{O^-}_{\diagdown O^-} & \quad ^-O - C \diagup^{O}_{\diagdown O^-} & \quad ^-O - C \diagup^{O^-}_{\diagdown O} \end{matrix} \right\}$$

Each oxygen atom is attached to the carbon atom by a bond that is a hybrid of a double bond (one-third) and a single bond (two-thirds). The three carbon-oxygen bonds are thus identical.

Calcium carbonate. The most important carbonate mineral is calcium carbonate, $CaCO_3$. This substance occurs in beautiful colorless crystals as the mineral *calcite* (Figure 7-6). *Marble* is a micro-crystalline form of calcium carbonate, and *limestone* is a rock composed mainly of this substance. Calcium carbonate is the principal constituent also of pearls, coral, and most sea shells. Calcium carbonate also occurs in a second crystalline form, as the mineral *aragonite* (Figure 7-7).

When calcium carbonate is heated (as in a lime-kiln, Figure 7-8, where limestone is mixed with fuel, which is burned) it decomposes, forming calcium oxide (*quicklime*):

$$CaCO_3 \longrightarrow CaO + CO_2 \uparrow$$

Quicklime is slaked by adding water, to form calcium hydroxide:

$$CaO + H_2O \longrightarrow Ca(OH)_2$$

Slaked lime prepared in this way is a white powder that can be mixed with water and sand to form *mortar*. The mortar hardens by forming crystals of calcium hydroxide, which cement the grains of sand together;

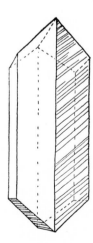

FIGURE 7-7

Natural crystal of aragonite, another form of calcium carbonate, $CaCO_3$.

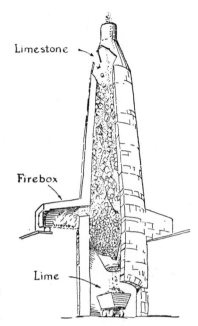

Limestone

Firebox

Lime

FIGURE 7-8

A lime-kiln.

then on exposure to air the mortar continues to get harder by taking up carbon dioxide and forming calcium carbonate:

$$Ca(OH)_2 + CO_2 \longrightarrow CaCO_3 + H_2O$$

Large amounts of limestone are used also in the manufacture of Portland cement, described in Chapter 26.

Sodium carbonate (*washing soda, sal soda*), $Na_2CO_3 \cdot 10H_2O$, is a white, crystalline substance used as a household alkali, for washing and cleaning, and as an industrial chemical. The crystals of the decahydrate lose water readily, forming the monohydrate, $Na_2CO_3 \cdot H_2O$. The monohydrate when heated to 100° changes to anhydrous sodium carbonate (*soda ash*), Na_2CO_3.

Sodium hydrogen carbonate (*baking soda, bicarbonate of soda*), $NaHCO_3$, is a white substance usually available as a powder. It is used in cooking, in medicine, and in the manufacture of *baking powder*.

Baking powder is a leavening agent used in making biscuits, cakes, and other food. Its purpose is to provide bubbles of gas, to make the dough "rise." The same foods can be made by use of sodium hydrogen carbonate and sour milk, instead of baking powder. In each case the reaction that occurs involves the action of an acid on sodium hydrogen carbonate, to form carbon dioxide. When sour milk is used the acid that reacts with the sodium hydrogen carbonate is lactic acid, $HC_3H_5O_3$, the equation for the reaction being

$$NaHCO_3 + HC_3H_5O_2 \longrightarrow NaC_3H_5O_3 + H_2O + CO_2 \uparrow$$

The product $NaC_3H_5O_3$ is sodium lactate, the sodium salt of lactic acid. Cream of tartar baking powder consists of sodium hydrogen carbonate, potassium hydrogen tartrate ($KHC_4H_4O_6$, commonly known as cream of tartar), and starch, the starch being added to keep water vapor in the air from causing the powder to form a solid cake. The reaction that occurs when water is added to a cream of tartar baking powder is

$$NaHCO_3 + KHC_4H_4O_6 \longrightarrow NaKC_4H_4O_6 + H_2O + CO_2 \uparrow$$

Baking powders are also made with calcium dihydrogen phosphate, $Ca(H_2PO_4)_2$, sodium dihydrogen phosphate, NaH_2PO_4, or sodium aluminum sulfate, $NaAl(SO_4)_2$, as the acidic constituent.

The leavening agent in ordinary bread dough is *yeast*, a microorganism. This microorganism produces an *enzyme* (an organic catalyst) that converts sugar into alcohol and carbon dioxide:

$$C_6H_{12}O_6 \longrightarrow 2C_2H_5OH + 2CO_2 \uparrow$$

The formula $C_6H_{12}O_6$ in this equation represents glucose, a simple sugar.

The Ammonia-Soda Process. Sodium carbonate is a very important chemical, over three million tons being made every year. About a quarter of the total amount is used in making glass, and another quarter in making soap, the rest being required in the textile and paper industries and many others. Nearly all of this great quantity of sodium carbonate is made from sodium chloride by a process called the *ammonia-soda process* or *Solvay process*.

This process depends upon the fact that sodium hydrogen carbonate is less soluble in water than are sodium chloride, ammonium hydrogen carbonate (NH_4HCO_3), and ammonium chloride.

The raw materials used in the process are sodium chloride and calcium carbonate (limestone), as well as coal to supply power and heat. The limestone is heated in a kiln, to produce carbon dioxide and lime (calcium oxide):

$$CaCO_3 \longrightarrow CaO + CO_2 \uparrow$$

The carbon dioxide is allowed to react with a solution of sodium chloride which has been saturated with ammonia; ammonium ion and hydrogen carbonate ion are formed in the solution:

$$NH_3 + H_2O + CO_2 \longrightarrow NH_4^+ + HCO_3^-$$

When a sufficiently large amount of carbon dioxide has dissolved in the solution, the solution becomes saturated with sodium hydrogen carbonate, which precipitates out:

$$Na^+ + HCO_3^- \longrightarrow NaHCO_3 \downarrow$$

The solid sodium hydrogen carbonate is filtered off, purified by re-crystallization, and dried. Most of it is converted into sodium carbonate, by heating it:

$$2NaHCO_3 \longrightarrow Na_2CO_3 + H_2O + CO_2 \uparrow$$

The carbon dioxide formed in this reaction is used along with that made from limestone to make more sodium hydrogen carbonate.

The low cost of sodium carbonate made by this process depends upon the fact that the ammonia can be practically completely recovered. At the end of the process, after the sodium hydrogen carbonate has precipi-tated out and has been filtered off, a solution of ammonium chloride remains. The calcium oxide obtained from the lime kiln is converted into calcium hydroxide by the addition of water, and the calcium hydroxide when added to the solution of ammonium chloride liberates ammonia:

$$CaO + H_2O \longrightarrow Ca(OH)_2$$
$$Ca(OH)_2 + 2NH_4Cl \longrightarrow CaCl_2 + 2H_2O + 2NH_3 \uparrow$$

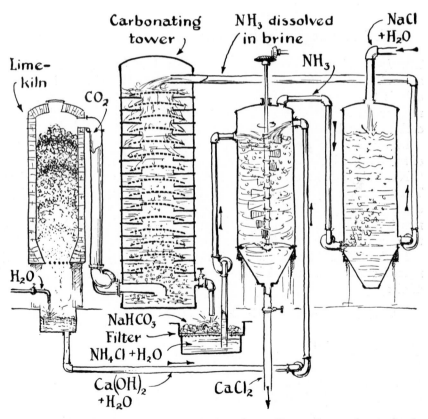

FIGURE 7-9 *Diagram of a chemical plant for making sodium carbonate by the ammonia-soda (Solvay) process.*

Hence the only substances used up in the process are limestone and common salt, and the only by-product (subsidiary substance produced in the process) is calcium chloride.

The large-scale apparatus used in this industrial process is illustrated in Figure 7-9.

Illustrative Exercises

7-3. A solution of carbon dioxide in water contains the following molecules and ions, in addition to H_2O and CO_2: H_2CO_3, H^+, HCO_3^-, CO_3^{--}. Write equations for the production of these substances. What are their names?

7-4. Write equations for two successive reactions of sodium hydroxide (solid) and carbon dioxide.

7-5. Write the structural formulas of carbonic acid and the carbonate ion.

7-6. Write equations for the preparation of quicklime from limestone and of slaked lime from quicklime.

7-7. Write equations for the two principal reactions that occur during the setting of mortar.

7–6. The Paraffin Hydrocarbons

The *hydrocarbons* are compounds composed of hydrogen and carbon alone. The simplest hydrocarbon is **methane, CH_4**. The methane molecule is tetrahedral, the four hydrogen atoms lying at the corners of a regular tetrahedron about the carbon atom, and connected with the carbon atom by single bonds (Figure 7-10).

Methane is a colorless, odorless gas. Some of its properties, and those of some other hydrocarbons, are given in Table 7-1.

Natural gas, from oil wells or gas wells, is usually about 85% methane. The gas made by destructive heating of coal or oil (Section 7–4) also consists largely of methane. The gas that rises from the bottom of a marsh is methane (plus some carbon dioxide and nitrogen), formed by the anaerobic (air-free) fermentation of vegetable matter.

Methane is used as a fuel. It is also used in large quantities for the manufacture of carbon black, by combustion with a limited supply of air:

$$CH_4 + O_2 \longrightarrow 2H_2O + C$$

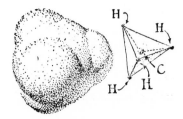

FIGURE 7-10

The structure of the methane molecule.

The methane burns to form water, and the carbon is deposited as very finely divided carbon, which finds extensive use as a filler for rubber for automobile tires.

Methane is the first member of a series of hydrocarbons called the *methane series* or *paraffin series*. Some of the compounds of this series are listed in Table 7-1.

The name paraffin means "having little affinity." The compounds of this series are not very reactive chemically. They occur in petroleum. The molecules heavier than ethane are characterized by containing carbon atoms attached to one another by single bonds. **Ethane** has the

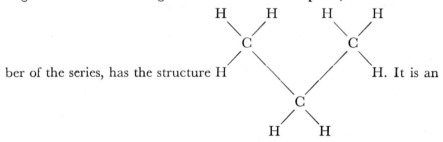

structure H——C——C——H. It is a gas (Table 7-1), which occurs in

large amounts in natural gas from some wells. **Propane**, the third member of the series, has the structure H   H. It is an

easily liquefied gas, and is used as a fuel.

In the structural formula for propane there is a *chain* of three carbon atoms bonded together. The next larger paraffin, **butane**, C_4H_{10}, can be obtained by replacing a hydrogen atom at one end of the chain by a

TABLE 7-1   *Some Physical Properties of Normal Paraffin Hydrocarbons*

SUBSTANCE	FORMULA	MELTING POINT	BOILING POINT	DENSITY OF LIQUID
Methane	CH_4	−183° C	−161° C	0.54 g/ml
Ethane	C_2H_6	−172	−88	.55
Propane	C_3H_8	−190	−45	.58
Butane	C_4H_{10}	−135	−1	.60
Pentane	C_5H_{12}	−130	36	.63
Hexane	C_6H_{14}	−95	69	.66
Heptane	C_7H_{16}	−91	98	.68
Octane	C_8H_{18}	−57	126	.70
Nonane	C_9H_{20}	−54	151	.72
Decane	$C_{10}H_{22}$	−30	174	.73
Pentadecane	$C_{15}H_{32}$	10	271	.77
Eicosane	$C_{20}H_{42}$	38		.73
Triacontane	$C_{30}H_{62}$	70		.79

methyl group, $-\overset{\displaystyle H}{\underset{\displaystyle H}{C}}-H$. Its formula is obtained by adding CH_2 to that

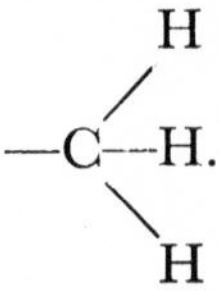

of propane. These hydrocarbons, with longer and longer chains of carbon atoms, are called the *normal paraffins*.

The lighter members of the paraffin series are gases, the intermediate members are liquids, and the heavier members are solid substances. The common name *petroleum ether* refers to the pentane-hexane-heptane mixture, used as a solvent and in dry cleaning. *Gasoline* is the heptane-to-nonane mixture (C_7H_{16} to C_9H_{20}), and *kerosene* the decane-to-hexadecane mixture ($C_{10}H_{22}$ to $C_{16}H_{34}$). *Heavy fuel oil* is a mixture of paraffins containing twenty or more carbon atoms per molecule. The *lubricating oils*, *petroleum jelly* ("vaseline"), and *solid paraffin* are mixtures of still larger paraffin molecules.

Isomerism.   The phenomenon of *isomerism* is shown first in the paraffin series by butane, C_4H_{10}. **Isomerism** *is the existence of two or more compound substances having the same composition but different properties.* (It is analogous to the allotropy of elementary substances, Section 6–10.) The difference in properties is usually the result of difference in the structure of the molecule, that is, in the way that the atoms are bonded together. There are two isomers of butane, called *normal butane* (*n*-butane) and *isobutane*. These substances have the structure shown below and in Figure 7-11; normal butane is a "straight chain" (actually the carbon chain is a zigzag chain, because of the tetrahedral nature of the carbon atom), and the isobutane molecule contains a branched chain:

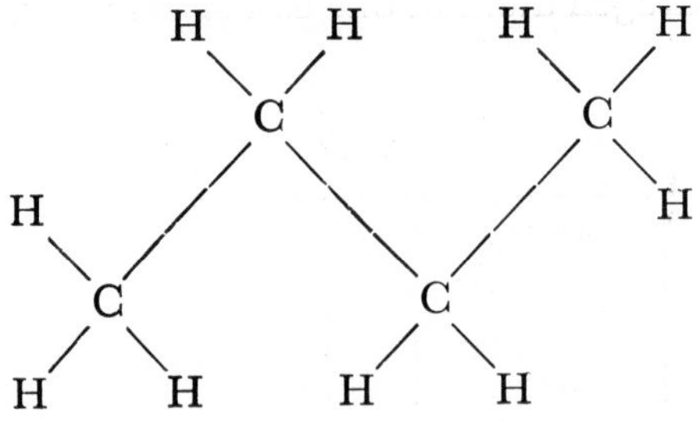

n-butane

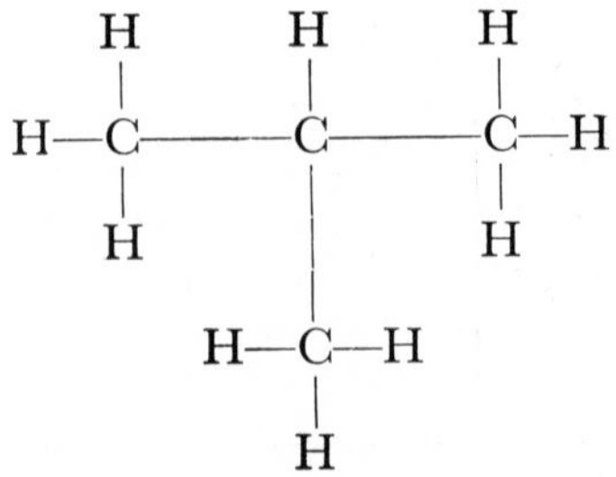

isobutane

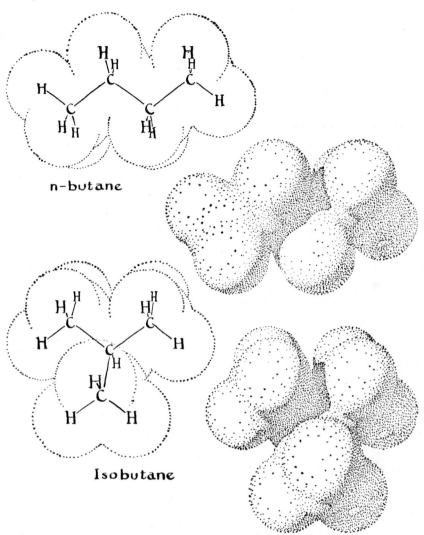

FIGURE 7-11   *The structure of the isomers normal butane and isobutane.*

In general, the properties of these isomers are rather similar; for example, their melting points are −135° C and −145° C, respectively.

The normal (straight-chain) hydrocarbons "knock" badly when burned in a high-compression gasoline engine, whereas the highly branched hydrocarbons, which burn more slowly, do not knock. The "Octane number" (the antiknock rating) of a gasoline is measured by comparing it with a mixture of *n*-heptane and a highly branched octane, with name 2,2,4-trimethylpentane and structural formula

The octane number is the percentage of this octane in the mixture with the same knocking properties as the gasoline being tested.

The substance *tetraethyl lead*, $Pb(C_2H_5)_4$, is widely used in gasoline as an antiknock agent. Gasoline containing it is called *ethyl gas*.

Names of Organic Compounds. Chemists have developed a rather complicated system of names for organic compounds. The student of general chemistry needs to know only a small part of this system.

The simpler substances usually have special names; for example, methane, ethane, propane, butane. From pentane on (Table 7-1) the names of the paraffins give the number of carbon atoms, with use of the Greek prefixes for the numbers.

The group obtained by removing a hydrogen atom from a paraffin has the name of the paraffin with the ending *ane* changed to *yl*. Thus the methyl group is $-CH_3$, the ethyl group is $-C_2H_5$ (as in lead tetraethyl, above), and so on.

A branched hydrocarbon is given a name, according to the system of nomenclature, that is based on the longest chain of carbon atoms in it. The carbon atoms are numbered from one end $(1,2,3, \cdots)$, and groups attached to them, in place of hydrogen atoms, are indicated. For example, the substance called isobutane above (in the discussion of isomerism) may be called 2-methylpropane. Another example is 2,2,4-trimethyl-pentane, the structural formula of which is given above in the discussion of knocking of gasoline engines.

7-7. *Hydrocarbons Containing Double Bonds and Triple Bonds*

The substance **ethylene**, C_2H_4, consists of molecules

$$\begin{array}{ccc} H & & H \\ \diagdown & & \diagup \\ & C\!=\!C & \\ \diagup & & \diagdown \\ H & & H \end{array}$$

, in which there is a double bond between the two carbon atoms. This double bond confers upon the molecule the property of much greater chemical reactivity than is possessed by the paraffins. For example, whereas chlorine, bromine, and iodine do not readily attack the paraffin hydrocarbons, they easily react with ethylene; a mixture of chlorine and ethylene reacts readily at room temperature in the dark, and with explosive violence in light, to form the substance *dichloroethane*, $C_2H_4Cl_2$:

$$C_2H_4 + Cl_2 \longrightarrow C_2H_4Cl_2$$

or

$$\underset{H}{\overset{H}{\diagdown}}C=C\underset{H}{\overset{H}{\diagup}} + Cl-Cl \longrightarrow H-\underset{H}{\overset{Cl}{\underset{|}{C}}}--\underset{Cl}{\overset{H}{\underset{|}{C}}}-H$$

In the course of this reaction the double bond between the two carbon atoms has become a single bond, and the single bond between the two chlorine atoms has been broken. Two new bonds, single bonds between a chlorine atom and a carbon atom, have been formed.

A reaction of this sort is called an *addition reaction*. An **addition reaction** *is a reaction in which a molecule adds to a molecule containing a double bond, converting the double bond into a single bond.*

Because of this property of readily combining with other substances such as the halogens, ethylene and related hydrocarbons are said to be *unsaturated*. Ethylene is the first member of a homologous series of hydrocarbons, called the *ethylene series*.

Ethylene is a colorless gas (b.p. $-104°$ C) with a sweetish odor. It can be made in the laboratory by heating ethyl alcohol, C_2H_5OH, with concentrated sulfuric acid, preferably in the presence of a catalyst (such as silica). Concentrated sulfuric acid is a strong dehydrating agent, which removes water from the alcohol molecule:

$$C_2H_5OH \overset{H_2SO_4}{\longrightarrow} C_2H_4 + H_2O$$

The formula H_2SO_4 is written above the arrow in this equation to show that sulfuric acid is needed to cause the reaction to take place.

Ethylene is made commercially simply by passing alcohol vapor over a catalyst (aluminum oxide) at about $400°$ C. The reaction is *endothermic;* * a small amount of heat if absorbed when it takes place:

$$C_2H_5OH \longrightarrow C_2H_4 + H_2O$$

Endothermic chemical reactions are in general favored by heating the reactants.

Ethylene has the interesting property of causing green fruit to ripen, and it is used commercially for this purpose. It is also used as an anesthetic.

Acetylene, which has the structural formula $H-C\equiv C-H$, is the first member of a homologous series of hydrocarbons containing triple bonds. Aside from acetylene, these substances have not found wide use, except for the manufacture of other chemicals.

Acetylene is a colorless gas (b.p. $-84°$ C), with a characteristic garlic-like odor. It is liable to explode when compressed in the pure state, and is usually kept in solution under pressure in acetone. It is used as a fuel, in the oxy-acetylene torch and the acetylene lamp, and is also used as the starting material for making other chemicals.

* Reactions that emit heat are called *exothermic*.

Acetylene is most easily made from **calcium carbide** (calcium acetylide, CaC_2). Calcium carbide is made by heating lime (calcium oxide, CaO) and coke in an electric furnace:

$$CaO + 3C \longrightarrow CaC_2 + CO \uparrow$$

Calcium carbide is a gray solid that reacts vigorously with water to produce calcium hydroxide and acetylene:

$$CaC_2 + 2H_2O \longrightarrow Ca(OH)_2 + C_2H_2 \uparrow$$

The existence of calcium carbide and other carbides with similar formulas and properties shows that acetylene is an acid, with two replaceable hydrogens. It is an extremely weak acid, however, and its solution in water does not taste acidic. The calcium carbide crystal is ionic; its structure resembles that of sodium chloride (Figure 4-6), with calcium ions, Ca^{++}, in place of the sodium ions, and acetylide ions, C_2^{--}, in place of the chloride ions.

Acetylene and other substances containing a carbon-carbon triple bond are very reactive. They readily undergo addition reactions with chlorine and other reagents, and they are classed as unsaturated substances.

7–8. *Some Other Organic Compounds*

The Chloromethanes. Methane and other paraffins will react with chlorine and bromine when exposed to sunlight or when heated to a high temperature. When a mixture of methane and chlorine is passed through a tube containing a catalyst (aluminum chloride, $AlCl_3$, mixed with clay) heated to about 300° C, the following reactions occur:*

$$CH_4 + Cl_2 \longrightarrow CH_3Cl + HCl$$
$$CH_3Cl + Cl_2 \longrightarrow CH_2Cl_2 + HCl$$
$$CH_2Cl_2 + Cl_2 \longrightarrow CHCl_3 + HCl$$
$$CHCl_3 + Cl_2 \longrightarrow CCl_4 + HCl$$

In each of these reactions a chlorine molecule, with structural formula Cl—Cl, is split into two chlorine atoms; one chlorine atom takes the place of a hydrogen atom bonded to carbon, and the other combines with the displaced hydrogen atom, to form a molecule of hydrogen chloride, H—Cl. Using structural formulas, we rewrite the first reaction:†

---

* The relative amounts of the four products may be varied somewhat by changing the ratio of methane and chlorine in the gas mixture used.

† It does not matter whether [structure] C [structure] or H—C—H is written for methane.

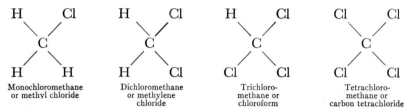

The four chlorine derivatives of methane, which are called the *chloro-methanes*, have the following individual names:

| Monochloromethane or methyl chloride | Dichloromethane or methylene chloride | Trichloro-methane or chloroform | Tetrachloro-methane or carbon tetrachloride |

Chemical reactions such as these four are called *substitution reactions*. A **substitution reaction** *is the replacement of one atom or group of atoms in a molecule by another atom or group of atoms.* The four chloromethanes are *substitution products* of methane. Substitution reactions and addition reactions (Section 7–7) are extensively used in practical organic chemistry.

Some physical properties of the chloromethanes are given in Table 7-2. All four are colorless, with characteristic odors, and with low boiling points, increasing with the number of chlorine atoms in the molecule. The chloromethanes do not ionize in water.

Chloroform and carbon tetrachloride are used as solvents; carbon tetrachloride is an important dry-cleaning agent. Chloroform is also used as a general anesthetic.

Care must be taken in the use of carbon tetrachloride that no large amount of its vapor is inhaled, because it damages the liver.

TABLE 7-2   *Some Physical Properties of the Chloromethanes*

SUBSTANCE	FORMULA	MELTING POINT	BOILING POINT	DENSITY OF LIQUID
Methyl chloride	CH_3Cl	$-98°$ C	$-24°$ C	0.92 g/ml
Dichloromethane	CH_2Cl_2	-97	40	1.34
Chloroform	$CHCl_3$	-64	61	1.49
Carbon tetrachloride	CCl_4	-23	77	1.60

Methyl Alcohol and Ethyl Alcohol.   An *alcohol* is obtained from a hydrocarbon by replacing one hydrogen atom by a hydroxyl group, —OH. Thus methane, CH_4, gives *methyl alcohol*, CH_3OH, and ethane, C_2H_6, gives *ethyl alcohol*, C_2H_5OH. The names of the alcohols are often written by using the ending *ol;* methyl alcohol is called *methanol*, and ethyl alcohol *ethanol.* They have the following structural formulas:

$$\begin{array}{ccc}
& H & \\
& | & \\
H-C-O-H & & \\
& | & \\
& H &
\end{array} \qquad \begin{array}{c}
H \quad H \\
| \quad | \\
H-C-C-O-H \\
| \quad | \\
H \quad H
\end{array}$$

Methyl alcohol   Ethyl alcohol

To make methyl alcohol from methane the methane may be converted to methyl chloride by treatment with chlorine, as described above, and the methyl chloride then converted to methyl alcohol by treatment with sodium hydroxide:

$$CH_3Cl + NaOH \longrightarrow CH_3OH + NaCl$$

Methyl alcohol is made by the destructive distillation of wood; it is sometimes called wood alcohol. It is a poisonous substance which on ingestion causes blindness and death. It is used as a solvent, and for the preparation of other organic compounds.

The most important method of making ethyl alcohol is by the fermentation of sugars with yeast. Grains and molasses are the usual raw materials for this purpose. Yeast produces an enzyme that catalyzes the fermentation reaction. In the following equation the formula $C_6H_{12}O_6$ is that of a sugar, glucose (also called dextrose and grape sugar, Chapter 30):

$$C_6H_{12}O_6 \longrightarrow 2CO_2 \uparrow + 2C_2H_5OH$$

Ethyl alcohol is a colorless liquid (m.p. $-117°$ C, b.p. $79°$ C) with a characteristic odor. It is used as a fuel, as a solvent, and as the starting material for preparing other compounds. Beer contains 3 to 5% alcohol, wine usually 10 to 12%, and distilled liquors such as whiskey, brandy, and gin 40 to 50%.

The *ethers* are compounds obtained by reaction of two alcohol molecules, with elimination of water. The most important ether is **diethyl ether** (ordinary ether), $(C_2H_5)_2O$. It is made by treating ethyl alcohol with concentrated sulfuric acid, which serves as a dehydrating agent:

$$2C_2H_5OH \longrightarrow C_2H_5OC_2H_5 + H_2O$$

It is used as a general anesthetic, and as a solvent.

The Organic Acids. Ethyl alcohol can be oxidized by oxygen of the air to **acetic acid**, $HC_2H_3O_2$ or CH_3COOH:

$$C_2H_5OH + O_2 \longrightarrow CH_3COOH + H_2O$$

This reaction occurs easily in nature. If wine, containing ethyl alcohol, is allowed to stand in an open container, it undergoes the acetic-acid fermentation, and changes into vinegar, by the above reaction. The change is brought about by micro-organisms ("mother of vinegar"), which produce enzymes that catalyze the reaction.

Acetic acid has the following structural formula:

```
  H        O—H
  |       /
H—C—C
  |       \\
  H        O
```

It contains the group —C with O—H and O (carboxyl group), which is called the *carboxyl group*. It is this group that gives acidic properties to the organic acids.

Acetic acid melts at 17° C and boils at 118° C. It is soluble in water and alcohol. The molecule contains one hydrogen atom that ionizes from it in water, producing the *acetate ion*, $C_2H_3O_2^-$. The acid reacts with bases to form salts. An example is sodium acetate, $NaC_2H_3O_2$, a white solid:

$$HC_2H_3O_2 + NaOH \longrightarrow NaC_2H_3O_2 + H_2O$$

Chemical Reactions of Organic Substances. In the above paragraphs we have discussed derivatives of methane and ethane in which a hydrogen atom is replaced by a chlorine atom, —Cl, a hydroxyl group, —OH, or a carboxyl group, —COOH. There are many other groups that can replace a hydrogen atom, to form other substances.

In general, the chemical reactions that can be used to convert methane into its derivatives can be applied also to the other hydrocarbons. By chemical analysis and the study of the chemical reactions of a new substance the chemist can determine its formula. For example, if a substance contains only carbon, hydrogen, and oxygen, and has acidic properties like those of acetic acid (its solution in water turns blue litmus red, it reacts with sodium hydroxide to form a salt), the chemist assumes that it contains a carboxyl group, —COOH. An important part of organic chemistry is the use of special reactions that identify different groups in a molecule.

Illustrative Exercises

7-8. Write the equation for the reaction of ethane and chlorine to form monochloroethane (C_2H_5Cl, also called ethyl chloride, a colorless gas, b.p. 12° C). What is its structural formula? Is there more than one isomer of C_2H_5Cl? (Answer: no)

7-9. Write the equation for the reaction of monochloroethane to form dichloroethane. How many isomers of dichloroethane do you predict? (Answer: two) What are their structural formulas?

7-10. What would you expect to be formed by the reaction of monochloroethane and sodium hydroxide? Write the equation for the reaction.

7-11. Write the equation for the reaction of addition of chlorine to ethylene, showing the structural formulas. How many isomers of the product are obtained?

7-12. Write the structural formulas of methane, ethane, propane, *n*-butane, and isobutane. Write equations for the burning (with oxygen of the air) of each of these substances.

7-13. What is the structural formula of dimethyl ether? Write the equation for its preparation from methyl alcohol and concentrated sulfuric acid.

7-14. What is the structural formula of the compound C_3H_8O that has the name methyl ethyl ether?

7-15. The name 1,2-dichloroethane is applied to the dichloroethane isomer in which the two chlorine atoms are bonded to different carbon atoms (the numbers 1,2, ··· are used to designate successive carbon atoms in a chain). Write the equation for the reaction of this substance with a large amount (an excess) of a strong solution of sodium hydroxide. (The product, called *ethylene glycol*, is used as an antifreeze agent in automobile radiators.)

7-16. Formic acid, HCOOH, is the first member in the series of carboxylic acids. (It can be obtained by distilling ants, and its name is from the Latin word for ant.) Write the equation for the preparation of formic acid by oxidation of methyl alcohol.

7–9. *The Carbon Cycle in Nature*

The atmosphere contains about 0.03% carbon dioxide. Additional carbon dioxide is being poured into the atmosphere all of the time—all animals exhale carbon dioxide, which has been produced by the oxidation of carbon compounds in their tissues, and carbon dioxide is also produced by the burning of wood and coal and the slow decay of plant and animal remains. If there were not some mechanism for removing carbon dioxide from the atmosphere, the composition of the atmosphere would in the course of time change enough to make the earth unsatisfactory for life in its present form.

There is a mechanism for the removal of carbon dioxide from the atmosphere: this mechanism is the utilization of atmospheric carbon dioxide by plants. The amount of plant life on the earth is such that a steady state has been reached, in which the content of carbon dioxide in the atmosphere has remained nearly constant for tens of millions of years. Through the cooperation of plants and animals there has been achieved a *carbon cycle* in nature.

Carbon dioxide is taken from the air by the plants, and broken down into carbon (in the form of *carbohydrates*, compounds of carbon with hydrogen and oxygen in the ratio H_2O), and free oxygen, which is liberated into the air. Some of the plants are burned or are oxidized during the process of decay, their carbon being returned to the atmosphere as carbon dioxide. Others are eaten by animals, and the carbon in the plant tissues is changed into carbon in the animal tissues. Ultimately the compounds of carbon in the animal tissues are oxidized, and the carbon is returned to the atmosphere as carbon dioxide in the exhaled breath of the animals, or the animal dies, and the carbon is ultimately returned to the atmosphere through oxidation to carbon dioxide during decay.

The carbon cycle in the form that is of most interest to man involves three steps: carbon dioxide in the atmosphere is converted into carbon compounds in the tissues of plants; the plants (or animals that have eaten the plants) are eaten by man, and the carbon compounds are converted into carbon compounds in the tissues of man; the carbon compounds are oxidized in the tissues by oxygen which has been inhaled, and the carbon dioxide that is produced is exhaled into the atmosphere.

Energy is required to convert carbon dioxide and water into carbohydrates (cellulose, starch, sugars) and free oxygen. This energy is obtained by the plant from sunlight. The process of using the energy of sunlight to carry out the reaction is called *photosynthesis:*

$$CO_2 + H_2O + \text{energy from sunlight} \longrightarrow (CH_2O) + O_2$$

The formula (CH_2O) is used to indicate that there are many units with composition CH_2O in the molecules of carbohydrates produced; a simple sugar such as glucose has the formula $C_6H_{12}O_6$. The reaction of photosynthesis that is carried out by plants is one of the most important of all chemical reactions.

It has not been found possible to carry out the reaction of photosynthesis in the laboratory. Early in the history of the world, however, nature found a way, by developing a special catalyst which is highly effective. This catalyst, called *chlorophyll*, is a complex substance containing magnesium ion. It is the green substance that gives the green color to the leaves of plants. Chlorophyll is green because it absorbs the light in the red-orange region of the spectrum (Section 28–6), and allows the green light to pass through or to be reflected. The energy of the absorbed light is used for the chemical reaction which is catalyzed by the chlorophyll.* This process of photosynthesis is one of the important ways in which man obtains energy from the sun.

There are great amounts of carbon dioxide, in combined form, in the sea and in rocks. Sea water contains about 0.15% of its weight in carbon dioxide, mainly as hydrogen carbonate ion, HCO_3^-. The total amount of carbon dioxide contained in sea water is about one thousand times as much as that in the atmosphere. Also, very large quantities of carbon dioxide are bound in carbonate rocks, especially limestone. We can understand that if the climatic conditions were to change somewhat large amounts of carbon dioxide might be released from the oceans and from rocks, and the concentration in the air might increase. It is probable that there were much larger amounts of carbon dioxide in the atmosphere during the Carboniferous Period that at the present time, and

* Chlorophyll has been found not to be active after it has been extracted from the plants.

that for this reason plant life flourished, permitting the great coal beds to be laid down.

Facts, Concepts, and Terms Introduced in This Chapter

Organic chemistry and biochemistry.

The structure theory of organic chemistry. Structural formulas (valence-bond formulas).

Diamond, graphite, charcoal, coke, carbon black. Structural formulas of diamond and graphite. Hardness; Mohs scale.

Carbon monoxide. Its action as a poison—carbonmonoxyhemoglobin. Uses.

Carbon dioxide. Its uses.

Fuels: anthracite coal, bituminous coal, coke, petroleum, coal gas, natural gas, producer gas, water gas.

Carbonic acid and the carbonates. Structure of carbonate ion—resonance theory. Calcium carbonate: calcite, marble, limestone, aragonite. Quicklime, slaked lime, mortar. Sodium carbonate (washing soda, sal soda, soda ash). Sodium hydrogen carbonate (baking soda, bicarbonate of soda). Baking powder. Yeast. Enzyme, an organic catalyst. The ammonia-soda process for making sodium carbonate.

The paraffin hydrocarbons. Methane, ethane, propane, butane, · · ·, a homologous series of organic compounds. Petroleum ether, gasoline, kerosene, heavy fuel oil, lubricating oil, petroleum jelly, solid paraffin.

Isomerism. n-Butane and isobutane. Knocking of internal combustion engines; octane number of fuel. Tetraethyl lead; ethyl gas.

Hydrocarbons containing double bonds and triple bonds. Ethylene; its preparation, properties, and uses. Unsaturated compounds; addition reactions with chlorine and other reagents. Acetylene. Calcium carbide.

Other organic compounds. Substitution reactions of paraffins. Methyl chloride, dichloromethane, chloroform, carbon tetrachloride. Methyl alcohol, ethyl alcohol. Fermentation; conversion of sugar into ethyl alcohol. Acetic acid, vinegar. Other organic acids —carboxylic acids. The carboxyl group. Reactions of organic substances.

The carbon cycle in nature. Photosynthesis, chlorophyll.

Exercises

7-17.   Compare diamond and graphite as to composition, hardness, density, structure, and principal uses.

7-18.   Compare carbon monoxide and carbon dioxide as to color, odor, solubility in water, physiological activity, and combustibility.

7-19.   Why is solid carbon dioxide popular as a refrigerating agent?

7-20.   Write the equation for the reaction of sodium hydrogen carbonate with hydrochloric acid. Do you think that baking soda and dilute hydrochloric acid (added separately to the dough) could be used in cooking in place of baking powder?

7-21.   Outline the successive steps in the ammonia-soda process for making sodium carbonate, and write equations for the reactions. What are the raw materials used, and what are the products?

7-22.   What is an addition reaction? A substitution reaction? Write an equation to illustrate each, using bromine, Br_2, as one of the reactants.

7-23. What are the principal substances in gasoline?

7-24. How many isomers do you predict for pentane, C_5H_{12}? Draw their structural formulas.

7-25. Propylene, C_3H_6, follows ethylene in the ethylene series. What is its structural formula? Write the equation, using structural formulas, for its addition reaction with chlorine.

7-26. What product would you expect to get if ethylene were allowed to react with chlorine at room temperature in the dark? At high temperature, with an excess of chlorine? Write equations.

7-27. Draw a structural formula for tetraethyl lead.

7-28. What are the principal uses of ethylene and acetylene?

7-29. Write equations for the preparation of calcium carbide from lime and coke and of acetylene from calcium carbide and water.

7-30. Write equations for the preparation of ethyl alcohol from ethane by use of chlorine and sodium hydroxide as reagents.

7-31. Write the equation for the fermentation reaction of glucose, $C_6H_{12}O_6$.

7-32. Ethylene glycol, mentioned in Exercise 7-15, can be oxidized to oxalic acid, $H_2C_2O_4$. Oxalic acid contains two carboxyl groups. What is its structural formula? It is a poisonous substance, which occurs in small quantities in some plants, such as rhubarb.

7-33. Write the equation for the acetic fermentation reaction, which converts wine into vinegar.

7-34. Make a diagram to illustrate the carbon cycle in nature.

References: Books on Organic Chemistry

J. B. Conant and A. N. Blatt, *Fundamentals of Organic Chemistry*, The Macmillan Co., New York, **1950**.

L. F. and M. Fieser, *Textbook of Organic Chemistry*, D. C. Heath Co., Boston, **1950**.

R. C. Fuson and H. R. Snyder, *Organic Chemistry*, John Wiley and Sons, New York, **1954**.

H. J. Lucas, *Organic Chemistry*, American Book Co., New York, 1953.

Roger J. Williams and Lewis F. Hatch, *An Introduction to Organic Chemistry*, D. Van Nostrand Company, Inc., New York, **1948**.

Many other good books on organic chemistry have been published.

PART TWO

Some Aspects of
Chemical Theory

In Chapter 1 we discussed different kinds of matter—homogeneous materials and heterogeneous materials, mixtures, solutions, and pure substances. In Chapter 2 a beginning was made on the correlation of the properties of substances and their structure, especially in relation to the atomic theory. We have seen that the characteristic properties of crystals are a consequence of their regular structure. A crystal of copper, which was discussed as an example, contains atoms of copper packed closely together in a regular three-dimensional arrangement, and a crystal of iodine, discussed as an example of a molecular crystal, contains molecules, each made of two iodine atoms, packed closely together in another regular arrangement. In a liquid the atoms or molecules are packed together, but not in a regular arrangement, and they are able to move around one another, permitting the liquid to flow, and to adjust its shape to its container. In a gas the atoms or molecules are free to move away from one another, permitting the gas to expand to fill the volume of its container.

In Chapter 3 the study of structure was carried one step further, to the structure of the atom itself. An account was given of the experiments that led to the discovery that the atom is not a fundamental particle of matter, incapable of subdivision, but is itself composed of simpler particles: each atom contains one nucleus, which has a positive electric charge, and one or more electrons, which have negative electric charges. Atoms are known in which the nucleus has a single unit of positive electric charge (hydrogen), two units of positive electric charge (helium), and so on, without a gap, to 100 units of positive electric charge (centurium). The number of electric charges on the nucleus is called the atomic number of the atom. The structure of the nucleus itself was also discussed: every nucleus can be described as composed of protons and neutrons (except the simplest one, the proton itself). The number of protons in the nucleus is equal to the atomic number of the atom. All of the atoms with a given atomic number constitute an element; 100 elements are known.

A substance composed only of atoms of one element is called an elementary substance, and a substance composed of atoms of two or more elements, in definite proportions, is called a compound; a discussion of the nature of elements and compounds was presented in Chapter 4.

The 100 elements differ greatly from one another in their properties, and the task of learning and remembering many of the important facts about them would be an appalling one if it could not be systematized. It is fortunate that the properties of the elements depend upon their atomic numbers in a systematic way, as expressed in the periodic law. In Chapters 5, 6, and 7 we have described the arrangement of the elements, the periodic table, that corresponds to the periodic law, and have discussed the properties of a number of the commoner elements, and their compounds, in correlation with the periodic table. An important concept, the concept of valence, which determines the composition of compounds, has also been briefly discussed. The dependence of the valence of an element on the position of the element in the periodic table provides a striking illustration of the value of the periodic law in systematizing the facts of chemistry.

We are now ready to embark upon a further study of chemical theory, which is presented in the following five chapters. We have learned, in the earlier chapters, that compounds are formed of atoms of different elements, in definite proportions: water, for example, consists of molecules containing two atoms of hydrogen and one atom of oxygen. We see that if we knew the relative weights of the atoms we could calculate the weights of hydrogen and oxygen in water—that is, the composition of water. Chapter 8 is devoted to this quantitative aspect of chemistry—weight relations in chemical reactions. The quantitative discussion of chemical reactions and of the properties of substances is then continued in Chapter 9, on the properties of gases.

The concept of valence is amplified in Chapters 10, 11, and 12. It has been found that the power of atoms to combine with one another is determined by their electronic structure. In some chemical reactions there is a transfer of electrons from one atom to another; some of these reactions are discussed in Chapter 10, which deals with ions, ionic valence, and electrolysis. The structure of molecules and crystals in which electrons are shared between two atoms is treated in Chapter 11, on covalence and electronic structure. A general discussion of chemical reactions involving electron transfer is presented in Chapter 12, on oxidation-reduction reactions.

When you have completed the study of Part II of this book, and have gained an understanding of these more quantitative and precise aspects of chemical theory, you will be in a position to proceed more effectively than before with the study of the properties and reactions of chemical substances.

Chapter 8

Weight Relations in Chemical Reactions

In every branch of chemistry it is necessary to make calculations about the weights of substances involved in chemical reactions; and sometimes calculations of this sort are of interest in every-day life.

These calculations can always be carried out by considering the atoms involved and using their atomic weights. No new principles are needed —the applications of arithmetic and algebra closely resemble those of the problems of every-day life. The only difficulty that the student might have is that of getting accustomed to dealing with such small objects as atoms and molecules.

Analyze each problem that you meet; do not memorize rules for solving these problems. When you have a problem to solve, think about it until you are sure that you understand it; in particular, consider the behavior of the atoms involved. Then formulate an equation containing the unknown quantities, making use of atomic weights, and solve it. It is often helpful to solve a problem in steps.

8–1. *The Atomic Weights of the Elements*

All of the weight relations in chemical reactions depend upon the weights of the atoms of the elements. These weights (or masses), called *atomic weights*, are very important in the study and practice of chemistry.

The Meaning of Atomic Weights. The fact that many elements consist of a mixture of stable isotopes complicates the discussion of atomic weights.

The chemical atomic weights of elements are the average relative weights (masses) of atoms of the elements, the average being for the usual isotopic composition of each element.

The base of atomic weights is the element oxygen, with its atomic weight arbitrarily taken as 16.00000. Oxygen was chosen as the base by general agreement of chemists for the reason that it combines with most of the elements, whose atomic weights can then be evaluated by the experimental determination of the weight relations involved in the oxygen compounds. The choice of 16.00000 is due to the facts that with this standard an astonishingly large number of elements have nearly integral atomic weights (carbon, C, 12.011; nitrogen, N, 14.008; sodium, Na, 22.997; etc.) and that none has atomic weight less than one unit (hydrogen, H, 1.0080; helium, He, 4.003; lithium, Li, 6.940). The atomic mass unit (atomic weight unit) is defined as exactly 1/16 of the mass of an average oxygen atom. The atomic weight of an element is the average mass of an atom of the element measured in this unit.

Ordinary hydrogen contains about one deuterium atom (mass 2.0143 units) to every 5000 light hydrogen atoms (mass 1.0078 units). We see that the extra mass, approximately one unit, of one deuterium atom to every 5000 light atoms would cause an increase in the average mass of 1/5000, or 0.0002 units, and that accordingly the average mass, or chemical atomic weight, of ordinary hydrogen is 1.0078 + 0.0002 = 1.0080.

The chemical atomic weight defined in this way, as the average for the usual isotopic composition of the element, would not be very useful unless the isotopic composition were constant. It is in fact found that the isotopic composition of most elements (the proportion of different isotopes) is the same for all natural occurrences of the element, to within the precision of experimental determination of atomic weights. An exception is lead, which is found in certain minerals (where it was formed by radioactive decomposition of thorium) with atomic weight 205.96 and in others (where it was formed from uranium) with atomic weight 208.0. The atomic weight of ordinary lead, from the common mineral galena, PbS, is 207.21. Since galena is the source of almost all the lead that is used, this is the value given in the table of atomic weights.

The History of the Atomic Weight Scale.   John Dalton, who in 1803 made the old atomic hypothesis into a useful scientific theory by developing the concept of atomic weights, chose as the base the value 1 for hydrogen. Later Berzelius, who made many atomic-weight determinations, used 100 for oxygen as the base; this was not accepted, and the Belgian chemist J. S. Stas in his careful work from 1850 on used the value 16 for oxygen, considering this equivalent to 1 for hydrogen. By 1905 it was recognized that the ratio of atomic weights for hydrogen and oxygen, as determined by measuring experimentally the ratio of weights of hydrogen and of oxygen that combine with one another to form water, differs from 1 : 16 by nearly 1 percent. Most of the experimental values of atomic-weight ratios had been determined relative to oxygen, for which 16

TABLE 8-1   *International Atomic Weights 1955*

NAME	SYM-BOL	ATOMIC NUMBER	ATOMIC WEIGHT*	NAME	SYM-BOL	ATOMIC NUMBER	ATOMIC WEIGHT*
Actinium	Ac	89	227	Mendelevium	Mv	101	[256]
Aluminum	Al	13	26.98	Mercury	Hg	80	200.61
Americium	Am	95	[243]	Molybdenum	Mo	42	95.95
Antimony	Sb	51	121.76	Neodymium	Nd	60	144.27
Argon	A	18	39.944	Neon	Ne	10	20.183
Arsenic	As	33	74.91	Neptunium	Np	93	[237]
Astatine	At	85	[210]	Nickel	Ni	28	58.71
Barium	Ba	56	137.36	Niobium	Nb	41	92.91
Berkelium	Bk	97	[249]	Nitrogen	N	7	14.008
Beryllium	Be	4	9.013	Osmium	Os	76	190.2
Bismuth	Bi	83	209.00	Oxygen	O	8	16.0000
Boron	B	5	10.82	Palladium	Pd	46	106.4
Bromine	Br	35	79.916	Phosphorus	P	15	30.975
Cadmium	Cd	48	112.41	Platinum	Pt	78	195.09
Calcium	Ca	20	40.08	Plutonium	Pu	94	[242]
Californium	Cf	98	[249]	Polonium	Po	84	210
Carbon	C	6	12.011	Potassium	K	19	39.100
Cerium	Ce	58	140.13	Praseodymium	Pr	59	140.92
Cesium	Cs	55	132.91	Promethium	Pm	61	[145]
Chlorine	Cl	17	35.457	Protactinium	Pa	91	231
Chromium	Cr	24	52.01	Radium	Ra	88	226.05
Cobalt	Co	27	58.94	Radon	Rn	86	222
Columbium: see Niobium†				Rhenium	Re	75	186.22
Copper	Cu	29	63.54	Rhodium	Rh	45	102.91
Curium	Cm	96	[245]	Rubidium	Rb	37	85.48
Dysprosium	Dy	66	162.51	Ruthenium	Ru	44	101.1
Einsteinium	E	99	[254]	Samarium	Sm	62	150.35
Erbium	Er	68	167.27	Scandium	Sc	21	44.96
Europium	Eu	63	152.0	Selenium	Se	34	78.96
Fermium	Fm	100	[255]	Silicon	Si	14	28.09
Fluorine	F	9	19.00	Silver	Ag	47	107.880
Francium	Fr	87	[223]	Sodium	Na	11	22.991
Gadolinium	Gd	64	157.26	Strontium	Sr	38	87.63
Gallium	Ga	31	69.72	Sulfur	S	16	32.066§
Germanium	Ge	32	72.60	Tantalum	Ta	73	180.95
Gold	Au	79	197.0	Technetium	Tc	43	[99]
Hafnium	Hf	72	178.50	Tellurium	Te	52	127.61
Helium	He	2	4.003	Terbium	Tb	65	158.93
Holmium	Ho	67	164.94	Thallium	Tl	81	204.39
Hydrogen	H	1	1.0080	Thorium	Th	90	232.05
Indium	In	49	114.82	Thulium	Tm	69	168.94
Iodine	I	53	126.91	Tin	Sn	50	118.70
Iridium	Ir	77	192.2	Titanium	Ti	22	47.90
Iron	Fe	26	55.85	Tungsten	W	74	183.86
Krypton	Kr	36	83.80	Uranium	U	92	238.07
Lanthanum	La	57	138.92	Vanadium	V	23	50.95
Lead	Pb	82	207.21	Xenon	Xe	54	131.30
Lithium	Li	3	6.940	Ytterbium	Yb	70	173.04
Lutetium	Lu	71	174.99	Yttrium	Y	39	88.92
Magnesium	Mg	12	24.32	Zinc	Zn	30	65.38
Manganese	Mn	25	54.94	Zirconium	Zr	40	91.22

* A value given in brackets is the mass number of the most stable known isotope.

† The English name of this element has been changed recently, by action of the International Union of Pure and Applied Chemistry.

§ Because of the natural variations in the relative abundance of the isotopes of sulfur the atomic weight of this element has a range of ±0.003.

157

had been used: by accepting 16.00000 for oxygen as base, no change in the older tables was needed, except for hydrogen.

It is good that the decision to accept oxygen as the base was reached, since only a few years ago (1938) the ratio of atomic weights H : O was revised from 1.0078 : 16 to 1.0080 : 16 as the result of more precise experimental work. If hydrogen were being used as the base of atomic weights this change would have required changes of almost all atomic weights by 0.02%, instead of only that of hydrogen, because most atomic weights had been determined by comparison with oxygen.

Prout's Hypothesis.   An imaginative physician and chemist, William Prout of Edinburgh and London, in 1816 suggested that all atoms are built of hydrogen, with all atomic weights multiples of that of hydrogen. At that time the available rough values of atomic weights showed in general no disagreement with this hypothesis, and Prout rejected as erroneous those few that did. As more accurate values were obtained, however, it became clear that Prout's simple hypothesis was contradicted by the facts; chlorine, for example, has the atomic weight 35.46, and boron 10.82.

Prout's hypothesis was revived by the discovery of isotopes; thus chlorine consists of two natural isotopes with mass numbers 35 and 37, and boron of two isotopes with mass numbers 10 and 11, in each case with nearly integral atomic weights and present in such relative amounts as to give the chemical atomic weight. It is now seen that Prout's idea contained a large element of truth.

The Einstein Equation and the Masses of Nuclei.   A striking property of nuclei is that *the mass of a heavy nucleus is slightly less than the sum of the masses of the protons and neutrons that combine to form it.* The reason for this is that during combination of the protons and neutrons a large amount of energy is released in the form of radiation. In consequence of the relativistic relation (the *Einstein equation*) between mass and energy, which is $E = mc^2$ (E = energy, m = mass, c = velocity of light), this release of radiation leads to a corresponding decrease in mass by about 1 percent (see Chapter 32). The change in mass that accompanies ordinary chemical reactions as a result of the emission or absorption of heat is too small to be detected.

The Values of the Atomic Weights. The 1955 atomic weights of the elements, as announced by the International Committee on Atomic Weights,* are given in Table 8-1.

8–2. *The Quantitative Meaning of Chemical Symbols and Formulas*

A symbol such as Cu is used to indicate the element copper, either in the elementary substance or in compounds. It also means a definite amount of copper—one atom or one atomic weight (63.54) in any weight unit (such as 63.54 g or 63.54 pounds). In particular, however, it is often used to mean one *gram-atom* of copper, 63.54 g.

Similarly a formula such as $CuSO_4 \cdot 5H_2O$ represents the compound copper sulfate pentahydrate, which contains the four elements whose symbols are involved in the atomic ratios indicated by the formula.

---

* Report of the Commission on Atomic Weights of the International Union of Pure and Applied Chemistry. This report is discussed in the *Journal of the American Chemical Society,* July 20, 1956.

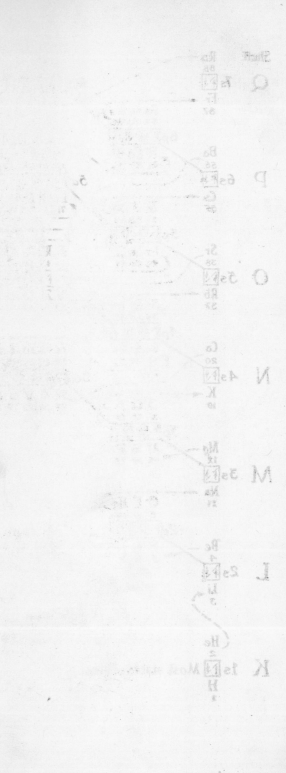